Mustang Roundup

Mustang Roundup

Written and Illustrated by Paul Laune

Holt, Rinehart and Winston
New York / Chicago / San Francisco

To my son Paul, my daughter Sidney, and my Unsworth grandchildren, all of whom I had the pleasure of putting on horses for the first time.

Contents

CHAPTER ONE

The Blaze-faced Mare

When I was a boy in northwestern Oklahoma the bad roads or no roads at all in some districts held back the motor age from our country, so almost everyone used horses. Of course, a few people owned cars, and more were chugging our way all the time.

For a boy it wasn't so bad to be living in the tail end of the "horse culture period." To get anywhere or to pull anything one needed a horse. To catch up with a strayed steer or a friend gone fishing along Spring Creek, one needed a horse. At that time horses fit very nicely into a boy's world.

Of course, there were many other animals running about on the farms and ranches and at some time or other, we boys of western Oklahoma met a variety of dogs, cats, donkeys, goats, heifers, cows, bulls, steers, mules, pigs, chickens, geese, and turkeys. Even some of the Texas longhorns were still around. Of them all, I managed to stay on best terms with the horses.

My biggest thrill came when my father, who was a lawyer and rancher, purchased several hundred mustangs while I was in my teens. These mustangs had been captured while running in wild bands in New Mexico and had then been shipped in railway stock cars to our town of Woodward.

1

The name "mustang" comes from the Spanish word *mesteño,* meaning unclaimed or belonging to the range. In early days in Texas, the word "maverick" came to have much the same meaning if one was talking about cattle. A rancher named Samuel Maverick had cattle spread over such a large range that many of his calves were not found and branded in the spring roundups. At the next roundup time when a cowboy found an unbranded yearling he might say, "It must be a Maverick," meaning that it must belong to Mr. Maverick. It wasn't long before the word "maverick" meant any unclaimed, unbranded calf or cow.

To be exact, the name mustang applies only to untamed, unowned, horses that live in herds like buffalo, deer, or antelope. However, men went on calling them mustangs, even after they were caught, broken, and trained into mannerly saddlehorses.

It was a big moment for us when each railway car was spotted at the stockyard chutes and the doors of the car flung open. Out of each car lunged forty wild-eyed, frightened, hungry and thirsty ponies. At every sudden noise or unexpected sight they jumped and started with the quick movements of squirrels. They snorted their fear and distrust. Cowboys said they had "rollers in their noses."

An auction was held and the ponies were sold in carload lots. The mustangs my father purchased were herded to a pasture not far from town, and there they were hazed into a big corral with a snubbing post in the center. The men who roped the broncs would hurriedly take a turn or two of their lariats around the snubbing post in order to hold the fighting animals.

Each mustang was roped and thrown to the ground, then scrubbed with a sheep-dip mixture to kill the ticks and disinfect him, and the cockleburrs were combed from his mane and tail. Sometimes during the following months the mustangs were roped again, this time to be broken to the saddle. Then followed many days of hackamore training and daily rides. All this was bewildering to the broncos at first, and it was a tough workout for their instructors, who had to ride out the bucks and lunges and runaways.

From each bunch of mustangs that came down the stockyard chutes, there were many that became gentle, dependable saddle ponies. A few were given more training for specialized work such as cutting steers from herds and helping a rider rope calves and steers.

Among the mustangs I found horse friends I will never forget. Blue, Spunky, Blaze, Fiddlefoot, and Buttons were good helpers and gentle members of the family. Others, such as Stirrup, were sort of friendly enemies. And one we called "the Blaze-faced Mare" almost broke my heart.

From them all I learned something about mustangs, about their habits and their manners. From ranchers and cowboys who had known them when they ran free, and who had captured and trained the mustangs, I added to my store of mustang lore. And from reading about the early Spaniards and the settling of North America, I learned where the mustangs came from and who their forefathers were.

Now, through this book, I hope to share with all who join in this mustang roundup, some of the interest those rare horses held for me.

One mustang mare my family once owned was a blood bay with a white blaze on her forehead that narrowed and ran down her face almost to her black muzzle. Her mane and tail were black, and she had white stockings on both forelegs. We had never gotten around to giving her a name, so we went on calling her the Blaze-faced Mare. My sister Russell, younger brother Benton, and I thought she was the most beautiful mustang that was ever brought to our pastures.

Everett Birch, a bronc tamer who sometimes came over to help out, looked her over and said, "If I ever see a gal that pretty, I'll ask her to marry me."

We always laughed at the way Everett talked, but we were pleased to see that he, too, liked her looks.

Dad suggested that we put off breaking her. I knew he wanted to have a hand in it. He so loved to work with horses, but at the time he was too busy at his law office and in court sessions.

"If we take it easy and are patient with this mustang mare, we can make her as gentle as a kitten." Then, after a pause, he asked, "What do you say? Shall we wait until we have more time, train her thoroughly, and then give her to your sister for a birthday present?"

His enthusiasm was catching. It wasn't as if I wanted the mare for myself. This way she would still be in the family. I had feared she might be sold. Anyway, I had my own ponies, Blue and Stirrup. I also rode Gale, but she belonged to Dad.

"What will we name her?" I asked.

"Oh, I don't know," Dad answered, and then thought a moment. "Why not let your sister have the pleasure of naming her?"

Weeks went by, and something always seemed to prevent our getting started with the breaking. Twice a week, it was my job to ride out after school, to the big pasture and check on the mustangs. It was not always easy to find every one. But sooner or later I would come on them in the gullies along Roundup Creek or hidden in the sand-hill thickets of sumac.

One day, I took a close look at the Blaze-faced Mare as she whirled and raced by. She was as fast and wild as a deer, but I had been close enough to note her condition. I had news to break to my Dad!

My finger followed down the pages of the tally book until I came to her listing. It read: Blaze-faced Mare . . . dark bay . . . both forefeet white . . . about 14 hands . . . 800 pounds. Then, on the opposite margin, I wrote, "Going to foal in the Spring."

I didn't need Dad to tell me the breaking of this mare would have to be postponed for quite some time.

Luckily, my sister knew nothing of the plans for her birthday present, so she was spared the disappointment of the delay. But for me the delay in starting the animal's training was galling. By making plans of her own, the mare had put a halt, for the time at least, to my pet project. Even football and the other activities of second year high school couldn't distract me completely.

Later on in the winter, I noticed the Blaze-faced Mare no longer stayed close to the herd. Being heavy with foal she was taking no chances of getting kicked in the belly by another horse. Sometimes it was almost dark before I found her among the wild plum and sumac thickets along the sandy river bed. Each time I went out it was harder to find her. Then, one overcast day late in March, I came upon her a mile away from the herd. It had snowed during the night and the ground was blanketed with white. In the snow, lying by the mare, was a splotch that looked dark and shapeless.

The sight of the colt just minutes old, lying in the cold snow, gave me a shock. My first thought was to get the delicate little thing up out of the snow. Dismounting some distance away I dropped the reins and left Blue ground tied. Then I walked slowly toward the mare with my hands palm out, making slow horse talk as I went.

I knew the range mare would be terrified, but I wanted to help her. Her eyes were blazing. Her head was thrust out toward me. Her legs were wide apart. She held her ground until I was within ten or fifteen feet, then the feral urge to run overcame her. A rolling snort ripped from her nostrils as she darted forty or fifty feet away. I picked the bundle up out of the snow and cradled it in my arms. The colt's legs slipped out and dangled beneath him. With a little help from me, he spread them out and struggled for balance. He teetered as if he was on stilts.

The mare was frantic. She moved closer and closer, snorting all the time. I had made a mistake in trying to help. The mare knew what to do and I didn't. The best thing, I realized, was to leave them both alone; so with a last steadying touch I left the foal weaving on his long legs. The excited, nickering mother rushed back to her colt, and I jumped on Blue and rode away.

Looking back, I was surprised to see that the colt was already nursing! A little being not ten minutes old, standing on his own feet, knowing how and where to nurse. It seemed like a miracle.

Six months passed before we got around to breaking the Blaze-faced Mare. Her nervy, handsome little son, with a white blaze on his face like his mother, cavorted about her when we ran her into the corral. We had been unable to cut her out of the bunch, so many other wild horses came in with her.

Dad was looking forward excitedly to the fun and tussle. He walked to the center of the corral by the snubbing post and began to shake out a loop in his lariat. I did the same. Some of the men on the place stopped what they were doing to sit on the top rail of the fence. Any sort of bronco roping makes a pretty good show.

The horses started milling as soon as Dad moved out from the snubbing post. He didn't whirl his loop overhead—he dragged it by his side, waiting for the Blaze-faced Mare to move out a bit from the pack. Suddenly he cast a "hoolihan." That's what some ropers called the sudden overhead throw used to catch horses in a corral. The loop seemed to spin open ahead of the mare, waiting for her to run her head into it.

As soon as he saw he had her, Dad made for the stout snubbing post and got a couple of dallies, or loops of the rope on it. The mare went back on the rope, fighting, lunging, and choking herself. With the rope wrapped around the post, Dad was able to hold her. We hoped we could avoid a hard fight. We didn't want this beautiful mare choked until she fell down from lack of air and exhaustion. We knew she must be thrown quickly. To do this and release the noose buried in her neck, her forefeet would have to be roped. That was where I came in. I was to rope her by the forefeet—

a throw called *mangana* by the Mexicans. Then I was to pull one way while Dad pulled the other. As soon as she hit the ground, I could rush in and put my knee on her neck. By reaching down and lifting her chin off the ground, she would be rendered helpless. In this way even a boy can hold down the wildest, most vicious bronco, and the choking rope can then be loosened. With a hackamore or rope halter slipped on her head, she can be allowed to get to her feet.

But it didn't turn out that way. Either I was too excited, or the dust was so thick I couldn't see the white legs flailing. My cast of the rope ended all our plans and hopes for the Blaze-faced Mare.

When I thought the loop had snared both forefeet, I came back hard on the rope. But somehow one foot was not caught or else managed to jerk free. With me pulling on one leg only, it spread her forelegs and she fell—spraddled out like a dancer doing a split. The fall broke her arm. The arm of a horse is the part we think of as the shoulder.

We knew almost instantly she was ruined. The rope was eased off the post, and the mare struggled to raise herself on her one good foreleg. Dad looked sick. He spoke for a minute to the men who clustered around, then turned abruptly and walked toward the barn. He said nothing as he went past me. His lips were clamped tight as if he were holding himself in. Did he think I had been careless, or too sure of myself? Was he thinking of the years he had spent schooling me in the handling of horses and ropes and guns?

I didn't care much what anyone thought just then. I was thinking of the beautiful Blaze-faced Mare who would never be gentled and trained, and I was trying not to let the men see me cry. The colt was whinnying. The other broncs were being hazed out of the open corral gate.

When Dad came out of the barn he was carrying a rifle. He held it out to me, stock first, and said, as though he were conferring a favor, "Here, you do it."

Without really knowing what I was doing, I took the gun. I turned away to see if the cartridge was thrown in the breech and the safety was off.

My thoughts were a whirling jumble. I had once put an old sick dog out of his misery with a bullet behind the ear . . . a steer once, when they were butchering on the Sand Creek place . . . lots of rabbits and quail . . .

The remembrance of some old code of Western horsemen even flashed through my mind about the duty of putting down your own horse when it was an act of mercy. But I can't—I thought—I can't pull the trigger on the Blaze-faced Mare. I don't know how long I stood there with my back turned to her.

It was Mr. Fred Hamilton, a crippled old man who at one time had been a top hand in the Panhandle, who took the gun out of my hand. Dad stepped over and took me by the arm and together we walked away. We were behind the barn when the gun went off.

After a while when I could talk, I asked, "What will we do about the colt?"

"Oh, let's see now," Dad spoke briskly and his hug tightened on my shoulder, "We'll keep him up at the barn and see that he is hand fed. He'll grow fast—be a big fellow in no time. What do you say—shall we call him Blaze after his mother?"

"Blaze," I tried it out. It seemed to fit all right. "And he'll be gentle— a regular pet when we start training him?" I looked questioningly at Dad.

"We'll make him into the best pony that ever looked through a bridle," Dad agreed.

CHAPTER TWO

The First Horses in America

Even today, a few mustangs manage to evade the horse hunters. In remote canyons and hidden valleys they run as free as deer, but there was a time when they ranged over the prairies by the thousands. In places they were as numerous as the buffalo once were. Mustangs are descended from Spanish horses, so to find out about them we must go back along their trails to the Spaniards who brought the first horses to the Americas.

In 1519, Hernán Cortés landed in Mexico with his army of five hundred and eight men. With them were sixteen horses—the first to set foot in North America. All were trained war horses of the Andalusian breed. Fortunately there was a soldier in Cortés' army who described every one of the sixteen head. His name was Bernál Díaz del Castillo. He thought that the horses, like the other fighters, rated a page in the history he wrote.

He mentioned "Bob Tail" and "Porcupine" and big black "Carrier," that Cortés rode. Five of the horses were mares and eleven were stallions. Two or three of them were especially fast. Another was fine for riding but not much good in a charge. Pedro de Alvarado, one of Cortés' most audacious lieutenants, owned a beautiful sorrel mare who was good for both.   *11*

One animal, Bernál wrote, was a "grand galloper." There were blacks and grays and chestnuts. One, a "parched sorrel," might have been what we call a Palomino.

The Spanish horses were very important. The conquest of Mexico was one of the most daring and fantastic quests the world has ever known, and that handful of horses spearheaded it.

When Cortés landed on Mexico's coast near Vera Cruz, he quickly learned of the gold and other wealth of the Aztec ruler, Montezuma. He learned that there were more people in the Aztec Empire than there were in the whole of Spain. He heard of the mines and the many productive farm districts. Later, he was to find beautiful cities with parks and zoos, and amazingly large and ornate buildings glistening in the sun.

Without hesitation Cortés decided to lead his small army inland to Tenochtitlán, the capital city of the Aztecs, in Mexico. He encountered desperately hard fighting, and the men on horseback were always in the lead. In a letter to his king, Charles I of Spain, Cortés told of the fierce charges: "For, after God, we owed the victory to the horses."

As the horses were killed in the many forays and were worn out on the long exploring trips, replacements arrived from the West Indies. During the twenty-seven years following Columbus' discovery of the West Indies, colonies had grown there, and horse raising had become a big business. Horses were the Spaniards' greatest war machine. The Aztecs and other Indians were terrified of them, for they had never seen anything like horses before. At first they thought the armored knight and his horse—also armored with shiny steel—was one horrible beetlelike monster. Some of them wondered if the horses were gods.

After Cortés had conquered the Aztecs and taken the city of Mexico, he turned south to subdue the people of Guatemala and Honduras. It was on this trip that one of his horses, Morzillo, came to be worshiped as a god.

The march south through unknown jungles and swamps had been difficult. Deep rivers had to be forded or bridged. Each day meant hacking out a trail deeper into regions never before seen by white men.

One morning, Cortés and his army came over a ridge and looked down green slopes into a lake. On an island in the lake they saw a glistening white city, which they later learned was Tayasal, the stronghold and capital of the Mayan tribe of Petén Itzá.

In the meadows near the shore, the many deer were a welcome sight to the Spaniards who had run short of food, and they wasted no time in starting the chase. The knights leaped on their fastest horses and spurred in pursuit. The sharp report of the foot soldiers' arquebuses echoed throughout the valley and across the lake.

The Mayan Indians were startled and offended by the attack. Deer were under the special protection of their god, Hubo, and on special occasions, to appease him, deer, and sometimes people, were slain and placed in front of the big bejeweled idol of Hubo. In their ignorance, the Spaniards had made a serious error. When Cortés rode up on Morzillo, the chief and his

priests and headmen bowed low. They looked intently at him and then at the big black horse. Morzillo was a proud animal. His glance at the Indians was haughty and dignified. The chief turned to Cortés and asked sternly why their deer had been killed.

Cortés saw the distress of the Indians and quickly said it was all an unfortunate mistake; that he and his men wanted to be friends. But the Mayas were puzzled. They had heard the guns and had seen the horses chase the deer. Why hadn't Hubo protected the deer, they asked themselves. They began to think that perhaps these strange beings with four legs had more power than Hubo; that maybe the horses were gods themselves.

After some talk with his followers, the head chief invited Cortés and his officers and Morzillo to pay them a visit in Tayasal. Cortés readily accepted. Thinking that his black steed would greatly impress the Mayas, who had never seen a horse before, he said he would be glad to bring Morzillo.

So, with about twenty of his closest companions walking at his side, Cortés rode Morzillo onto the barge for the short trip to the island city. The sight that greeted the Spaniards was fantastic. Great *teocallis* (pyramid temples) could be seen towering beyond the flat roofs of the dwellings. At the top of each pyramid was an ornate chapel. When the party landed, crowds of Indians clustered about them. Questioning their important leaders and priests, the people stared mostly at Morzillo. They were sure that he was responsible in some way for the flashes and smoke of the guns and the thunderous noise. They decided he must be the god of lightning and thunder.

To the Mayas Morzillo was a god who could be ferocious if he wanted to be. As with all their gods they felt they should placate him. But poor Morzillo wasn't feeling at all ferocious. His foot hurt. He was beginning to limp badly. Some days before he had injured it on a jagged rock and now it was throbbing and swelling. Sixty-eight other horses in the army had been so badly injured crossing the sharp stony ridges of the mountains that they had to be destroyed.

Now Cortés saw that Morzillo, too, would have to be left behind. It is possible that he brought him to the island city for that reason. He asked the chief if he would care for Morzillo until he could come by for him on his return trip. The Mayas were delighted to have such an important guest, and readily agreed to give Morzillo the best of care.

That evening, as Cortés and his friends started back to the army camp on the shore, they turned for their last glimpse of Morzillo. They saw the big black charger in the center of an admiring crowd. Children were fanning him with big leaves. Someone had braided green and yellow feathers into his mane. People were offering him fruit and food of all kinds. Even *tortillas,* dipped in the fiery chili sauce, were being held to his mouth. Flowers were heaped before him.

And that was the last that Cortés ever saw of his great horse. Cortés stayed in Honduras much longer than he had expected, and was unable to go through Tayasal on his way back to Mexico.

More than a hundred years went by before white men again visited Tayasal. Then, one day some missionaries, with a large party of soldiers and guides, rode south from Mexico to the remote lake of the Petén Itzás. The Mayan Indians that came to meet them seemed awestruck. They appeared more fascinated by the horses than the riders. Bowing low before the travel-worn and shying beasts, they touched their fingers to the ground and then lifted them to their lips. Courteously, they asked the strangers to come with them to their city on the island in the lake.

The *padres* and their party were overwhelmed by the large city with its many pyramid temples. Twelve of these temples, they said, had room enough in front of each for a thousand people to stand. Imagine their amazement when they saw the idol that stood atop the largest pyramid of all. It was a huge horse. His name, they were told, was "Tziminchec," the god of lightning and thunder. His eyes flashed with jewels, and his blocklike body was a mosaic of precious stones, gold, and pearls. Strangely, he was sitting down on his haunches like a dog.

For a moment Padre Bartólome Fuensalida and Padre Juan de Órbita gazed in wide-eyed disbelief. Then Padre Bartólome flew into a rage. He whirled on the chiefs and the Mayan priests and rebuked them for worshiping such an idol. It is said that he even called for his companions to bring hammers, and while they made a protective circle about him, he tried to destroy the monstrous thing.

All this happened long, long ago, but even today the legend of this horse god persists. Over the ruins of the old city of Tayasal there is today the shabby town of Flores. One of the most trustworthy authorities on the Spanish horses, Robert M. Denhardt, in his book, *Horses of the Americas,* says that the men of Flores, who row visitors across the Lake Petén Itzá in their canoes, tell of the god named Tziminchec who once sat on the highest temple in the old city. They say his home now is deep in the waters of the lake. On certain nights when the moonlight shines in just the right place, they say he can be seen.

Did the Mayas, who were too weak to oppose the might of the Spaniards, sink their god of lightning and thunder in the lake to save him from the wrath of Padre Bartólome? And do you suppose it is true that he is still there?

There is another curious thing about the statue of Morzillo that seems never to have been considered. Why was he sitting down like a dog? A horseman's logical answer is that very sick horses often sit that way, and

it is possible that Morzillo got sick and sat that way before he died. The Mayas, in making the statue thought, perhaps, that the sitting position he assumed was as natural as any other for a horse.

Years after Morzillo died, Spanish missionaries and the settlers who went with them took Spanish horses northward into country that later was to become the southwestern part of the United States. The horses they took multiplied until they were so numerous that many of them escaped from their masters and became ownerless mustangs, free to roam wherever they wished. We can almost imagine a dignified mustang saying to a rambunctious colt, "Walk proudly! Remember; long, long ago, one of your ancestors was worshiped as a god."

CHAPTER THREE

A Heritage of Courag

After conquering the Indians in Honduras, and leaving a garrison of Spaniards there to govern them, Cortés returned to Mexico. There he and many other Spaniards set up plantations and ranches in the rich Mexican valleys. Much attention was given to the horse ranches. Good blood stock was brought in from the West Indies and from Spain.

One of Cortés's ranches was called Vista Hermosa, which means Beautiful View. There one can still see the medieval splendor of the vine-draped buildings with their stern battlements. It is now a resort hotel and everything has been remarkably well repaired and cared for.

When Antonio de Mendoza came to Mexico as viceroy in 1535, he, too, developed many stock ranches. One of them, for horse raising only, took up the entire valley of Ulizabal. Mendoza is said to have given away over three hundred trained horses to friends. Eighty loads of hay were needed every day to feed the saddle horses he and his *caballeros* kept in Mexico City.

The Spanish horses raised by Cortés and Mendoza, and the other horse ranchers of Mexico, were sometimes called Andalusian horses or Cordova horses because they came from those districts in the southern part of Spain.

At the time they were considered the finest of all saddle horses, which meant, of course, they were also the best war horses.

Their training and careful breeding had started in the dim past. In their veins ran the blood of the Arabian horses and also of the Barbs of North Africa.

Where the Arabian horses first came from is a great mystery. All we know is that at about the time Jesus was born, the Arabians east of the Mediterranean Sea became raisers of wonderful horses. What adds to the mystery is the fact that when these Arabian horses were first noted by historians, they were the same fixed type of animal they are today, perhaps even bigger.

These horses were treated almost as though they were human members of the nomadic tribes. Sometimes they were allowed to live in the tents of their owners, and the horses with the purest blood were shown great respect by the people and were called "nobles." Noble sires were allowed by their owners to mate with none but noble mares. Constant rivalry went on between neighbors to see who could raise the best strain of horses. Numerous petty wars served as a training ground for the fleet, hot-blooded, desert-bred horses and truces were often made so the tribesmen could stop fighting long enough to go to big fairs and further test the speed and stamina of their mounts in horse races. For hundreds of years this careful, almost fanatical, horse raising program went on.

Under the religious and military leadership of the prophet Mohammed, the Arabian tribesmen united and took the name of Mohammedans. Their fighting was now directed against the Christian countries and in the year A.D. 670, long after the death of their leader, they started on a great two-pronged western advance across Africa and Europe.

When the Mohammedans reached the Barbary coast in North Africa they found themselves in a land of excellent horses, worthy of being mated with their own Arabian horses. These horses of Barbary, called barbs, were hot-blooded desert horses who, like the Arabian horses, could live on dry and sparse pasturage. Also like the Arabians, they had flint-hard hoofs and teeth. They had slender legs and small trim feet—small heads with eyes set wide apart and small neat ears that turned inwards. Their bodies were short-coupled and compact and they had wide chests that gave them good balance on the forelegs. Some students of horse history think the Arabians and the Barbs might have had common ancestors in prehistoric times.

In a very short while the two breeds—the Arab and the Barbs—blended. It was this new type of horse, the Arab-Barb, that the Mohammedans took to Spain when they invaded that country in A.D. 711. The Mohammedans who had joined with the Moroccans, or Moors, on the northwest coast of Africa, were soon known as Moors.

Moorish ranches were started quickly in Andalusia in Southern Spain. One district around Cordova produced so many excellent specimens that they were called Cordova horses. The Spaniards captured all they could from the Moors and started raising the Arab-Barb horses on their own ranches.

Fiercely the Spaniards fought to drive the Moors from their land and back to Africa. Battles and skirmishes were fought by men on horseback, in a war that lasted almost eight hundred years! No strain of horses has ever had such rigorous and consistent training.

Rodrigo Díaz de Bivar, the great Spanish leader who was called El Cid, rode a marvelous Arab-Barb stallion named Bavieca, which he had captured from King Yucef of Morocco. The Soldan of Persia sent El Cid another magnificent stallion in order to win his friendship and persuade him not to join in the crusade against the Mohammedans. These and other stallions owned by El Cid founded a strain of aristocratic Andalusian horses.

The Moorish wars went on and on until, in the very year that Christopher Columbus discovered the West Indies, the Spanish armies of Ferdinand and Isabella overcame the Moors and forced them back to Africa. All this happening in 1492 seems a miracle of timing, for as the war with the Moors ended, throwing a horde of Spanish knights and soldiers out of jobs, a new world across the western ocean opened up for them. Eagerly men hurried to the ports to find passage to the new lands. Soldiers, knights, settlers, stockmen, craftsmen, clerks, priests, lawyers, and overseers, set out to seek fortunes and to convert the people of the new lands to the Christian religion. With them on the high-pooped caravels went Arab-Barb horses, now generally called Spanish horses. Ahead of these Spaniards lay the West Indies and two unknown continents filled with undreamed of adventures and dangers. What the Spaniards were setting out to do would have been impossible without their amazingly hardy horses.

After the islands of Espanola, Puerto Rico, Cuba, and Darien on the isthmus of Panama were colonized, Cortés and other leaders went on to explore and conquer the mainland of the Americas. Ponce de León twice fought for a foothold in Florida and was killed by Indians on the second try. His discouraged colonists returned to Cuba. Pedro de Alvarado's horsemen conquered the Indians of Guatemala. Francisco Pizarro and his hard-riding, gold-hungry knights swarmed into Peru and made themselves master of the lands of the Incas. Nuño de Guzmán brutally ravaged the districts north and west of Mexico City. Tall, one-eyed, Pánfilo Narváez with handsome Cabeza de Vaca along as paymaster, led a band of fortune seekers inland from the west coast of Florida. In their many fights with the Indians, half of their horses were killed. Near starvation, they ate the remaining horses. Then, hoping to sail across the Gulf to Mexico, they started out in crude boats they had built.

Storms wrecked all of Narváez's boats on the coast of Texas in the vicinity of what is now called Galveston. De Vaca and three companions were the only survivors of the ill-fated expedition. These four Spaniards were made slaves by the Texas Indians and forced to wander with them for seven years before they reached the Spanish settlements on the west coast of Mexico. De Vaca later wrote of having seen great herds of humped-backed cattle, which were undoubtedly buffalo. Also he had heard of walled Indian cities with houses three and four stories high. He said seven such cities of great wealth were rumored to be in a land called Cibola.

The number *seven* caused the Spaniards in Mexico (or New Spain as it was now called), to take notice. All had heard the many legends that told of seven mysterious cities which were fabulously rich. To find them was the dream of every knight and fortune hunter.

So many men wanted to go in search of the cities that Viceroy Mendoza, who had been sent to govern New Spain by King Charles of Spain, formed them into an army. To lead this army he selected the young, handsome Francisco de Coronado. In the spring of 1540 Coronado led his army up the west coast of Mexico in the direction of what is now the United States. In this army were two hundred and fifty knights, five hundred and fifty-eight war horses, and many foot soldiers and Indian allies. Droves of cattle and sheep were taken along to feed the expedition. It was the largest army of explorers ever seen in this hemisphere. Unfortunately, the trip was a failure—at least it was a failure for the men who sought gold and wealth, because they found none. As an exploring trip, however, it was worthwhile, for they learned the lay of a vast new land, met different kinds of Indians and saw the strange buffalo. A small party of adventurous knights made a side trip westward and came upon the Grand Canyon. They were the first white men ever to look down into its awesome depths.

About the time Coronado's army was traveling across what was to be, almost four hundreds years later, the state of Oklahoma, Hernando de Soto was searching for gold with a large force just a few hundred miles to the east. He had landed in Florida with an army of almost a thousand men and two hundred and fifty horses.

All through the years of exploration, the very lives of the adventurous Spaniards were dependent on the wonderful endurance and stout hearts of their horses. The brown horse Coronado rode more often than any of his other mounts on his three-year journey was still going strong when Coronado rode him into Mexico City on his return.

Although none of the horses of Coronado or De Soto remained to live in the lands they explored, Spanish horses of the same excellent strain were later taken by Spanish missionaries and settlers to the region destined to become the southwestern part of the United States. These were the horses that escaped from the mission pastures, and from Indians who had stolen them, to form the wild mustang herds.

A story about a young man named Gonsalo de Sylvestre, and about his horse Peceño, shows the heritage of courage and the fighting will to live of the Spanish horse. De Soto once ordered Gonsalo to lead a party of horsemen to carry messages back to the base camp. The mission meant traveling for days through a trackless wilderness. Gonsalo was riding his beautiful horse Peceño, who next to the magnificent Azietuñiero, De Soto's own olive-colored charger, was the best war horse in the army. He was a chestnut whose white blaze ran all the way down his face to his mouth. And to Moorish and Spanish horsemen, a horse that "drank the blaze," as they put it, was sure to have strength and courage.

Almost before Gonsalo and his men were out of gunshot of the camp their troubles began. Angry, frightened Indians lurked behind the bushes. Spurring and dodging away, the knights felt the jolt of the arrows clunking and glancing off their steel armor. Sometimes it was only the speed of their horses that saved them from being caught and killed. They depended on their horses' bold lunges to help them plow a way with their lances through densely packed hordes of Indian warriors.

One day the party came, hungry and weary, to an icy river. Yelling savages stood on both banks. While some horsemen fought off the Indians, others pushed into the water, using makeshift rafts to float their armor across. Thus unhampered, their mounts swam beside them. When the Spaniards reached shallow water on the other side they slipped into their cold breastplates and scrambled up the bank fighting for a beachhead. The last man to cross was Gonsalo, who had remained to guard the rear because he had the best horse. With a last sally, he chased back the Indians, then whirled Peceño and plunged into the river. Clinging to his mane, Gonsalo slipped from the saddle to lighten the load. When it seemed Peceño's strength would surely fail, his hoofs hit bottom and he started to struggle up out of the water. Gonsalo eased into the saddle, and unstrapped his lance and shield. Then with his great heart pounding, Peceño came lunging up the bank. Now Peceño deserved a rest and he needed it badly, but the spurs were again raking his sides. Peceño did not hesitate. With all his strength and inbred will, he charged into the howling mass of warriors as he and Gonsalo joined their hard-pressed companions. Keeping in close formation, the knights pushed on and escaped from the pursuing Indians.

Never knowing when they would be attacked by other Indians, the young horsemen dared not stop for long to rest and sleep and hunt for something to eat. Two men died in their saddles, more from lack of food and sheer exhaustion than from the minor arrow wounds they had received.

Before they reached the supply camp, the last grains of corn the men carried were given to the horses to keep them going. Every horse lived to reach the camp.

Only a few weeks later, the valiant blaze-faced chestnut, Peceño, made his last charge. Pierced by an arrow, he crumpled to the ground at the very feet of the Indian who shot him. But even in this final charge he carried his rider to victory. The Indian was struck by Gonsalo's long lance.

Gonsalo was one of the survivors of De Soto's ruinous expedition. On crude ships that he and the others managed to build, about 300 men sailed from what is now Arkansas down the Mississippi River to its mouth. There they turned west and, following the coast, eventually reached the Spanish settlement of Pánuco in New Spain, which is now Tampico, Mexico.

It was not long before Gonsalo was back in the saddle. This time, however, he was fighting against his own countrymen in Peru. After his arrival there he had been forced to take sides in the endless conflicts carried on by Pizarro's greedy, warring captains. Again he was teamed with a spirited war horse. This one also possessed the will to survive. The determination to fight for life was stronger in the Spanish horse than in any other known breed. This fighting spirit lived on in its descendents, the mustangs and the cow ponies.

Day after day Gonsalo and his horse charged in and out of skirmishes, until one day they found themselves in the middle of a desperate battle. The blows and thrusts hammered and clanged, steel on steel. Under him his horse was a lunging fury, biting and striking out with his forefeet. Then in a flashing glimpse he saw that the animal was badly wounded. His face had been chopped open above the muzzle, and the canopy bone above one eye was smashed and broken by the blow of a mace. Blood streamed from his chin. As the suffering horse wheeled, he received two more wounds at the hands of a foot soldier who rushed in and stabbed at his forearms and chest.

Gonsalo thought that his own death was near, and he was certain that his mount had but a moment of life left in him. But the instinct to survive is strong in all creatures. Seeing an opening, Gonsalo broke from the mêlée. Capture meant certain death to Gonsalo. To his surprise, the gallant horse under him responded to the spurs and struggled into a swamp, where he kept going until he gained solid ground. The horses of his enemies, also weakened by severe injuries, were unable to follow closely.

Still expecting his horse to drop dead any second, Gonsalo urged him on for several miles before they both were hidden by the falling darkness. They were in the Andes mountains and it was bitterly cold. Gonsalo was tired, wounded badly, utterly discouraged, and cold and hungry. He looked at the bloody face of his poor charger. Carefully he slipped off the bridle. The horse's eyes, one almost closed, were blazing with rage. Then he lowered his head and "ate with so much fury that he pulled up the grass roots and ate them earth and all, and Gonsalo was comforted by seeing his horse eat."

It was as if the horse was saying, "You can give up and die if you want to—but for me, I'll show them—I'm going to live." And he did live, and so did Gonsalo for many years after that.

CHAPTER FOUR

The Missions and the Mustan

Long before the discovery of the New World, the bitter fighting against the Moors had set the Spanish character. Almost eight centuries of raids and counterraids had made them fierce fighters and had drawn the Spanish people closer together as a nation. It also had taught them greed. The gold and finery and ornate palaces of the luxury-loving Moors awaited any man, they had learned, who was strong enough to go out and fight for them. The constant exercise of war also had perfected the greatest war machine known to the age of knighthood—the Andalusian or Spanish horses.

The long fight against the Moors, who to the Spanish were enemies of Christ, also had instilled in the stoutly armed Spanish chivalry the firm belief that they, above all others, were the champions of the true Christian faith. So, when the new lands opened up for them across the Western Ocean, the Spaniards, in addition to seeking wealth, considered it their duty to convert the heathen Indians or be killed in the attempt. And, as it turned out, wherever they went, aided by their superb horses, they made themselves masters.

28   Not only in religion, but in language, architecture, stock raising, and

many other ways, the stamp of Spanish culture was put on an area of the Western World greater than all of Europe. Almost a hundred years before an English colony was firmly planted in North America, the Spaniards were well established in New Spain—the name they gave to Mexico. From the beginning, a steady stream of new settlers with trade goods and livestock poured in to New Spain from old Spain and the West Indies. Men with the pioneering urge pushed out in all directions from Mexico City, hoping to become owners of mining and ranch land. Members of aristocratic Spanish families were awarded immense land grants in New Spain. The Roman Catholic Church also was granted great tracts of land for missions and church farms and ranches. A few of the wealthiest and most important men were appointed by the Spanish king as governors of whole new provinces. That this land was already occupied by Indians made no difference; the Indians simply went with the land. When they were subdued they became wards, if not actual slaves, of the new landlords. Under this system the treatment of the Indians depended largely on whether the overlords were kindly and farsighted, or cruel and greedy.

When a governor was appointed to open up a new province, he first went out with a party of horsemen guided by some friendly Indians, and explored the country. Everyone in the party, except the Indians, rode on horses or mules. The poor Indians had to trudge along on foot. The Spaniards had passed a law prohibiting Indians from riding, or even getting up on a horse's back. The Spaniards knew what an awesome fighting weapon the horse was, and they did not want the Indians to learn how to use it. The Indians handled the horses, and curried and fed and watered them, but that was all. To break this law would have brought a penalty of death. However, it seems that few magistrates gave out sentences that severe.

When the party reached the area they were to make into a province, the

Indians they found there were often quite friendly—if they had heard little or nothing about the Spaniards. As curious and wide-eyed as children, they gathered around the new arrivals. Usually it was the horses that excited the greatest interest and wonder. As the Indians lost some of their fear of the beasts, they came closer and touched them. To them the horses were like big dogs. The Indians burst forth with a flood of questions and eagerly waited for the guides to explain. They felt the same wonder the Aztecs, Mayas, and other tribesmen had experienced many years before when the Spaniards had first appeared with their horses.

When the site was picked for a settlement, the priests in the party erected a large cross, before which they held masses. Shortly after, a priest who had been chosen by the Roman Catholic Church to supervise a large district started the building of a church and mission. From ranches nearer to Mexico City large herds of horses, cattle, sheep, and mules were brought to stock the pastures of the new mission.

A story of one herd of livestock that was taken to a new settlement in 1570 shows how rapidly animals increase when allowed to run wild. The colonists had not been in the new valley long when the Indians rebelled and chased them all out. Twenty years went by, and the Spaniards came back to try to settle there again. This time, to their surprise, the Indians seemed glad to have them back. To their even greater surprise, they saw large herds of cattle and horses, grazing in the surrounding valleys. There were now ten thousand animals, where there had been only about one thousand at the time they were forced to leave. The Indians were contented and well-fed, but they had killed and eaten only what they needed. In twenty years, the sons and daughters of the blooded livestock that had been raised and cared for on ranches such as those owned by the Cortés, Coronado, Oñate, and Mendoza families, were now as untamed and carefree as wild animals. The Spanish horses had become mustangs—perhaps the first to be mentioned in history.

In 1598, a big jump north was made. King Philip II of Spain appointed Don Juan de Oñate governor of the lands explored by Coronado. The new province was named New Mexico. Don Juan was the richest man in New Spain. From his father he had inherited large ranches and the fabulously productive Zacatecas gold and silver mines in the mountain region north of Mexico City. In addition he had married an heiress—the great-grand-daughter of both Montezuma and Cortés.

Don Juan was wealthy enough to start his new venture on a big scale. With four hundred men, many of whom brought wives and children, he struck out northward across the Province of Chihuahua. Trailing behind this long winding column of people were eighty-three wagons loaded with supplies, and seven thousand head of cattle, sheep, horses, and mules. With him also traveled several priests and lay brothers of the Church.

Far up the Rio Grande past the present town of Santa Fe, he founded his town, which he named for his patron saint, San Juan. A church was built —the second in what was to become the United States. The first church was built in 1565 in St. Augustine, Florida.

In order to explore his new domain, Oñate rode with thirty horsemen as far east as Kansas and as far southwest as the mouth of the Colorado River.

On his way back to the Rio Grande, he camped one night by a sandstone cliff rising two hundred feet above the surrounding country. To the Spaniards it looked like a lofty, battlemented, Moorish tower, and they gave it the name of El Morro. On its sheer wall, Oñate or one of his men scratched a message in the stone. It is still readable, and perhaps it is the oldest "name on wall" writing in the United States.

PASSED BY HERE THE COMMANDER
DON JUAN DE OÑATE FROM THE
DISCOVERY OF THE SOUTH SEA
ON THE 16TH OF APRIL, YEAR 1605

The South Sea that is mentioned is the Gulf of California.

When Don Juan returned east of the Rio Grande, he founded the town of Sante Fe within the walls of a mission that had been started. This was in 1605, two years before the English landed at Jamestown. Oñate made Sante Fe the capital of his Province of New Mexico, but he stayed only a short while to rule as governor before he returned to New Spain.

For seventy-five years the missions, towns, and ranches started on both sides of the Rio Grande, between Santa Fe and the southernmost town of San Juan, prospered. Oñate's town of Sante Fe was to become the "Spanish Horse Capital of the West." The very beginning of the Indian horse culture period was in New Mexico with Spanish horses. Later, when asked by the explorers and traders where they got their horses, the Indians said the "big dogs" were brought to their country by the "black robes." The horses had been brought by the padres, dressed in black clerical robes, to stock the mission ranches.

The church played a big part throughout all the pioneering and settling of the new country. It was not an easy task to teach and convert the Indians to Christianity, but the devoted Jesuits, and later the Franciscans, never faltered.

To house their churches and missions the brothers labored over drawings and plans and taught native craftsmen how to build. In Mexico and the southwestern part of the United States a few of these first structures are still standing. They are monuments to the blending of two cultures; the Indian craftsmen who labored on them, and the Spaniards who supervised and directed the Indians. Beautiful, ornate Spanish doorways, windows, or entire façades are set like jewels in the plain Indian adobe structure of the walls.

A mission was a place of refuge and a place of modest comfort. It was something like a fortress built onto and around a church. It also can be likened to an oasis in a desert. Some of the missions had touches of beauty and elegance. Some had cloisters and gardens with shade trees to add to their charm and sense of repose. They were reminders of old Spain far across the sea. The high walls that enclosed the buildings gave to the missions the look of small medieval towns, surrounded by the outlying farms and ranches of the Spanish settlers.

From the time they first arrived in New Mexico, the missionaries, and all the Spaniards, had to deal with two very different kinds of Indians; the more peaceful Pueblo Indians, who lived in permanent villages, and the warlike Indians who had no permanent homes and who lived by hunting. The Pueblo Indians as they are still called, such as the Taos, Hopi, Acoma, and Isleta, continued to live in their walled towns and to till their small fields just as they had before the Spaniards arrived. Being farmers they dared not risk being driven from their corn and cotton and melon patches and their permanent adobe homes. They even managed to keep the peace with most of the wild, roving Indians who came to their pueblos to trade hides and game for the corn and pottery and cloth that the Pueblo Indians produced.

Many of the mild-mannered Pueblo Indians went to the missions to learn the ways of the white men. Inside the walls, in busy, self-supporting shops, the Indians were taught various kinds of crafts and chores; cooking and housekeeping, leatherworking, carpentry, and cabinet making. They learned how to be jewelers, pottery and tile makers, masons, weavers, dyers, blacksmiths, horse doctors, gardeners, and even nurses in the small hospitals. And by about 1650, the law prohibiting the Indians to ride horses was no longer enforced, so Indians began to do the work of *vaqueros* or cowboys. For all this labor the Indians received little beyond the food they ate and a few other necessities.

As the years went by the docile Indians watched and pondered the austere, yet theatrical rituals of the padres. A few of the Indians were converted to Christianity and some, whether or not they grasped the meaning of the new faith, became deeply attached to the padres and lived out their lives near the missions as faithful followers and servants.

In contrast to these civilized Indians there were the other kinds, like the roving Comanches and Apaches who came occasionally to trade with the Pueblos. From the very beginning they were hostile to the Spaniards and they always remained so. Another tribe, the Navahos, were a special problem because they were viciously warlike, leaving their hogan villages to the northwest to attack both the Pueblo Indians and the Spaniards.

Even the "big dogs"—the horses—that were so fascinating at first— had only one interest for the wild Indians—that was to eat them, not to ride them. As the herds on the ranches increased, many stray horses fell victim to Indian arrows. The Indians hunted them down like any other game. Naturally, as the braves learned more about horses, they were smart enough to be on the lookout for a gentle horse to steal. A horse that could be led away would carry his own meat into camp. It wasn't long before young bucks learned to get on the backs of tame horses and to ride. We may be sure that the first one to ride a horse back to his camp was greeted like a returning hero.

Both the Pueblo Indians and the hostile tribes liked the livestock and the trade goods the Spaniards brought. They were captivated by the colored beads, the tiny tinkling bells, the metal cooking pots, and the bright silk and velvet cloths. The warriors' eyes gleamed as they handled the knives and hatchets and metal arrowheads. But there was one thing they didn't like. They didn't like to have the Spaniards bossing them around. Most of the Pueblo Indians resented having the Spaniards interfere in their customs and beliefs.

The Pueblo Indians were sun worshipers and had many minor nature gods. They held rites for the rain god, the harvest god, and others just as the Spaniards prayed to their many saints. Indian converts sometimes pretended to accept the religion of the priests simply to please, and the priests became angry when it was discovered that they were still taking part in tribal ceremonies.

The punishment meted out to the Indians for heathen idol worship, as the priests called it, was often severe. One young chief of the pueblo of Teguas, named Po-pé, seethed with indignation at the high-handed actions of the Spaniards. As he gained power as a chief, he grew more determined to lead his people in a revolt against Spanish rule. With another young chief, who used the Spanish name of Antonio Bolsas, he rode from pueblo to pueblo, stirring the smoldering anger of the Indians against the Spaniards.

By 1680 (many Indians rode horseback by this time), a large number of Pueblo Indians had joined the conspirators, and a date was set for a provincewide uprising. The Comanches and Apaches needed no urging to join in the attack on the white settlements. Only a few Indians remained loyal to the Spaniards. One was a chief called Juan de Ye, who warned his Spanish friends about the rumored revolt, but his warning was not taken seriously. So the Spaniards were utterly unprepared when, in 1680, every settlement in the province of New Mexico was attacked on the same day by the Indians. With the exception of several prisoners that were taken, all Spaniards were either killed or forced to flee New Mexico. Po-pé, the leader of this revolt, and his second in command, Bolsas, were the first horse-riding Indian leaders known to history.

Governor Otermin and the largest party of Spanish survivors fought their way down the Rio Grande, where at last they found refuge below El Paso del Norte.

Not a vestige of Spanish culture remained in all of New Mexico. In the one town of Isleta one hundred twenty Spaniards and mission Indians were killed and their large herds of livestock run off by the Apaches. This raid seemed to the Apaches an easy way to get rich and from then on, they were known as raiders and stealers of livestock. During the uprising the Apaches and Comanches got so many horses that they were soon trading them to other tribes, some as far east as the Gulf of Mexico.

For nearly fourteen years the Indians of New Mexico were free of the Spaniards. Then a large avenging army marched north from New Spain, overcoming all hostile Indians in its path. Instead of staying together to form a strong defensive force, the tribes scattered. The Comanches and Apaches retreated to the vast plains. After a short resistance the Pueblo Indians were subdued. The walled town of Santa Fe was taken by the Spaniards, and since Po-pé was no longer alive, it was Chief Bolsas who led the Indians in their losing fight. Bolsas was captured and executed. Never again did the Pueblo Indians revolt, but they have carried on a passive resistance to all white men ever since.

The untamed Plains Indians were to roam their buffalo lands for another one hundred and fifty years before they would give in to the white man's civilization.

The menace of the Horse Indians slowed, but did not stop, the courageous missionaries. One of the most remarkable of these was a Jesuit named Eusebius Keuhne, an Austrian by birth, who took the Spanish name of Padre Kino. His early training as a map maker was very useful to him when he explored and mapped the wild region of Sonora, New Spain, where he had been sent to found a mission. He arrived in New Spain in 1681 and for the next thirty years he devoted his life to ministering to the Indians. His days began before the sun was up, and were spent visiting Indian villages where he taught, held masses, baptized babies, married couples, and gave last rites to the dying. During his long trips on horseback or on muleback he seemed tireless. Long after dark he would unsaddle and see that his tired beast and himself had something to eat. Then, weary to the bone, he would fall asleep on a bundle of sheep skins. On one round trip he made to Mexico City to report to his Bishop, he rode fifteen hundred miles in fifty-one days. Even during this arduous journey, in the early mornings and late evenings, he carried on his work with the Indians. On his night journeys he was well able to guide himself by the stars, because among his other accomplishments he was an astronomer.

The only mission that still exists in the southwest between the Colorado River and the Rio Grande is San Xavier del Bac, in Arizona. When Padre Kino founded it in 1701, he had fourteen hundred head of livestock driven up from his Sonora headquarters. Many of the horses of Padre Kino eventually roamed away or were run off by Indians to become wild mustangs. Thus, Padre Kino, too, had a part in establishing the mustang herds of the West.

Another great missionary in the southwest was the Franciscan, Padre Garcés. From his headquarters at San Xavier del Bac, he set out to find a route to the California missions that were being started by Padre Junipero

Serra. On Padre Garcés' journeys, between 1769 and 1780, he crossed the Colorado River and the hazardous Mohave Desert five times. His diaries show that he visited over twenty-five thousand Indians of nine different tribes and traveled over five thousand miles.

A young Captain Juan Bautista de Anza followed the trails explored by Padre Garcés and deserves credit for leading the colony that left Santa Fe, New Mexico, to found San Francisco. Captain de Anza had taken on a great responsibility. Under his command was a cavalcade of soldiers and men and women settlers and their children. Following along were one hundred and sixty-five pack mules laden with baggage and with presents to placate any unruly Indians they might encounter. Behind these mules came five hundred and thirty horses, and strung out in the rear were three hundred and fifty-five cattle. The route they were to follow covered fifteen hundred miles of plains, mountains, and deserts. The Colorado River and the Mohave Desert were fearful obstacles. After weary months of travel the colonists came safely to the shore of San Francisco Bay. There was much rejoicing. Not a person or animal had been lost on the entire trip! The year was 1775.

The five hundred and thirty horses spread out on the lush grass of Alta (upper) California. Because there were no fences, many of them got away from the herders and grazed where they pleased. Twenty years after the founding of San Francisco, herds of California mustangs were a common sight.

CHAPTER FIVE

The Horse India

In California the Indians were seldom hostile. The lives of whole tribes soon centered around the newly established missions. But in New Mexico, as we have seen, a different situation existed. After being reconquered in 1694, the Pueblo Indians remained peaceful but withdrawn, while from all sides the wild maurading Horse Indians were a constant threat to the missions and the ranches.

Before the Spaniards came, the North American Indians had but two living creatures tame enough to keep about their lodges: dogs and wild turkeys. The dogs helped in every way they could, by running down game, sleeping on top of the beds at night to keep the people warm, and guarding the camp. Indian dogs were trained never to bark; they only growled their warnings. On hunts, dogs carried bundles of meat and hides strapped on their backs, and when camp was moved the squaws loaded them with packs. Dogs were handy to have around for another reason—Indians thought they were good to eat. Even the mountain men who were served dog meat by their Indian hosts would smack their lips and say, "Heap good!"

It may have been quite natural, at first for the Indians to think of horses as "big dogs," but the Indians never dreamed of what great changes in their lives these animals of greater size were to bring. Now, with really "big dogs" to ride, they could go racing across the prairie like the wind. With a horse under him, a hunter could range over far more country after game. From horseback, using arrows and lances, hunters could kill more buffalo than they had been able to afoot. So to the Indian, a horse was something of great value, something that could multiply, making him rich and important. The horse became an Indian status symbol.

Gradually the roving Indians stopped killing horses for food. With mounts they were able to kill all the buffalo they wanted, and they really preferred buffalo and dog to horse meat.

Following the revolt of the Indians in New Mexico in 1680, the news of the Spanish horses traveled like a prairie fire from tribe to tribe. Over the plains and up along both sides of the Rocky Mountains the talk was all about the "big dogs." Next to the arrival of the white man, it was the most startling news ever to reach the Indians. In big tepees, hundreds of miles from Santa Fe, tribal councils were held. Scouts were sent to get a good look at the strange animals. Raiding parties soon followed, hoping to steal a few from other tribes. From tribe to tribe, either by trade or theft, the horses moved out on new trails in all directions. The Comanches and Apaches, because they were close to the source of supply at first, dominated the trade in horses. From the Comanches the Kiowas of western Oklahoma got horses, and only a few years later, tribes to the north, the Cheyennes, Arapahoes, Pawnees, Sioux, and other tribes were riding Spanish horses.

Only seven years after the Indian uprising in New Mexico, the French explorer La Salle came to East Texas. He was there to scout the land to see if France could gain a foothold in the Spanish region of the Southwest. There, in 1687, he met Indians whose horses were marked with Spanish brands. He traded hatchets and glass beads for five horses. Thus, La Salle's was the first party of white men ever to trade for horses with the Indians. Although La Salle's venture in Texas was a fiasco ending with his murder by his own men, French trading posts were set up along the Arkansas River. Here the Indians traded their buffalo robes, beaver pelts, and stolen Spanish horses for tobacco, fancy clothes, liquor, guns, gunpowder, lead, candy, and numerous other articles. Some of the Spanish horses the traders got were sold across the Mississippi River to the Chickasaw Indians. Soon the fame of the fast Chickasaw "Indian ponies," which were horses of pure Spanish blood, began to filter into the English colonies of Virginia and the Carolinas. Through trade with the Indians the planters got some of the Chickasaw ponies and, by mating them with their English horses, produced a type of running horse that was very quick on the getaway. The planters called them Quarter Horses because they were so speedy in quarter-mile races. The English colonists also took Spanish horses during the many attacks they made on the Spanish settlements in Florida.

By 1730, most of the Plains Indians had horses, and their herds were increasing each year. Even so, the Indians continued a brisk trade in stolen Spanish stock. As late as 1805, when Meriwether Lewis and William Clark were on their exploring trip to the Pacific Ocean, they bought thirty horses from the Shoshone tribe, most of which had Spanish brands. Farther west, in the land of the Nez Percé, they noticed Spanish brands on both horses and mules. Thus it is evident that the Indians, even after having used horses for seventy-five years, still found it easier to steal tame horses from the Spanish ranches of New Mexico than to raise and break their own.

When the capable Captain Anza returned to Santa Fé from California, in 1776, he was made Governor of New Mexico. Several times he had to lead his cavalry against the Comanches and Apaches, who had been Horse Indians ever since the great raid of 1680, almost a hundred years before. Once Captain Anza managed to catch up with the Comanches after a raid, and in quick determined action his troopers recovered five hundred stolen horses.

The gradual spread of Spanish horses to the north; dates indicate their arrival in certain areas or first use by Indian tribes.

The defiant Comanches were back within a month to steal another two thousand horses.

The Spaniards realized there was no way to conquer the Horse Indians, who had no tribal capital that could be captured. Without permanent homes, their tepee villages could move between sundown and dawn. There were no boundaries to the Plains Indians' domain. Any army pursuing them would be swallowed up by the immense space. So the Spaniards watched their herds as best they could and tried to get along with their violent neighbors.

Had the Indians banded together they could easily have run all the Spaniards back to Mexico (after independence from Spain was won in 1821, it was no longer called New Spain), and could have taken all their horses. Later, when asked why they did not do it, an old chief answered with a grin, "We let the Spaniards live here so they could raise and break horses for us."

The time came, of course, when Indians had to raise and train their own horses. And when they did, many tribesmen took great pride in their horsemanship. The better Indian horsemen rode with the arrogance of kings. They regarded any man afoot as no man at all.

The Nez Perce and the Cayuse tribes became famed as horse raisers, having first gotten horses around 1725. Like the Arabians of the past, their horsemen selected the best and speediest sires and mares in order to produce fast-running, long-winded horses. They also favored and raised colorfully spotted horses called pintos, and dark roans with white rumps splattered with black spots—today called Appaloosas, a very popular saddle breed.

Most Indians were passionate gamblers. They loved horse racing, were often shrewd judges of horses, and were willing to make large bets on their favorites. Many white men learned some of the finer arts of horse racing from them the hard way.

CHAPTER SIX

A Cayuse Horse Race

Some of the finest and fastest horses of the Northwest were in the country bordering on the Umatilla River in Oregon. A large area called Umatilla Reservation was set aside for the Walla Walla, the Umatilla, and the Cayuse Indian tribes, when the country began to fill up with American settlers. Of the three tribes, the Cayuse Indians had the fastest and hardiest horses, and they also had more than any other tribe. At one time their horses numbered over twenty thousand head. Cayuse Indian ponies became so widely known, it was common practice to call any western horse a "cayuse."

Shortly after the Civil War ended a new Superintendent of Indian Affairs, Mr. A. B. Meacham, was appointed. He was a bluff, outspoken Irish-American. As a pioneer boy in Iowa he had known and liked Indians. In his travels west to the California gold fields, and then on to Oregon, he had learned to speak several tribal languages.

He felt the Indians had been badly treated by the government, and as superintendent he tried in every way to help them. He fostered a feeling of trust between the white men and the red men. But trust, Mr. Meacham always warned, ended on both sides when it came to horse racing. Any chicanery in that kind of contest appealed as much to Mr. Meacham's frontier style of humor as it did to the Indians'. He enjoyed seeing a shrewd deal with the Indians backfire on the white man who tried to cheat them.

In his book, *Wigwam and Warpath,* Mr. Meacham told about his close Indian friend, Chief How-lish-wam-po of the Cayuse tribe, called the "King of the Turf"in the Umatilla country. He was the outstanding horse rancher of the tribe, and his passion for horse racing and betting was well known.

Hidden away from the eyes of the white men, the chief had a pasture where he raised his race horses. The colts of his fastest sires and dams were carefully guarded in the pastures, and when they were two years old their training began. In Indian fashion, they were never stabled or grained or fitted with shoes. Seldom were they even curried. They were trained to respond with amazing quickness, yet they were easily managed. Each day the ponies were run to build up endurance, wind, and speed. Their time was checked on measured tracks, and each horse was prepared for the distance he seemed best suited for.

The chief's pride in the stamina and fleetness of his horses knew no bounds. He once told Mr. Meacham he had many horses that would carry a big man one hundred miles in one day and bring him back in the next. If the chief liked a man, he would sell him a good, well-trained animal. One lawyer friend of the chief bought a pony from him that could gallop thirty-one miles to the Columbia River in two hours. Mr. Meacham bought a small Cayuse mare for five dollars from the chief for his young daughter. The mare was so gentle and trustworthy that she became a family pet.

Men who were unfriendly with the Indians usually got the worst of any horse deal. One pompous man in town who treated the "Injuns," as he called them, with great disdain, bought a horse from the chief. When the pony was delivered, the easy way in which the Indian boy rode him made the pony seem mannerly and docile. From a leather shop nearby, the new owner had the pony outfitted with a fancy new saddle and bridle. Then in the midst of a crowd that had gathered, the new owner stepped up and mounted his steed to try his paces. He was a very dignified man in a long Prince Albert coat and a bell-topped derby hat on his head. He spoke to the pony to move out. Nothing happened. He slapped at the pony with the rein ends. Still nothing happened. He was becoming embarrassed. Now he brought his heels back hard. His long legs caused him to kick the pony in the flanks. The next instant he was sailing over the pony's head like a big black crow, his coat tails fluttering like wings. The pony went tearing out of town, headed for the reservation. He was found there later, but the saddle and bridle were never recovered.

When men with race horses started out to the reservation "to have a bit of fun with the Injuns," Mr. Meacham always warned them, "Be careful or you will lose your money." He wrote, "Poor fellows, I felt sorry for them." And sure enough, in most cases the men came riding back to town on scrubby Indian ponies, ponies the chief had given them out of charity, because he had won everything they had, including their race horses. Of course, the white men did manage to win a race now and then.

At one race, Joe Crabb, a prominent town sport, timed the chief's fastest racer, a pinto. The horse showed speed but seemed to tire toward the end of the race and was beaten. What Joe didn't know was that the chief had planned to have his pinto lose while Joe was watching. He was looking forward to a race with the thoroughbred he had heard Joe was importing from Kentucky, and was already scheming to win.

Joe's horse arrived from Kentucky. Joe clocked him and was pleased. Now, he thought, he had a horse that could show his heels to the Cayuse pinto.

When he saw the Kentucky horse, Chief Howlish was openly impressed. He pretended uncertainty now about racing his horse in such fast company, but in the end he allowed himself to be talked into a horse race. A date was set.

The Umatilla flats race course was a two-and-a-half mile stretch from the starting point to a post around which the horses turned to make the dash back. Thus the total distance was five miles; a grueling race for the best of horses.

On the day of the race, every rancher, soldier, clerk, government worker, trader, and banker in the area made some flimsy excuse for leaving work and headed for the Umatilla flats. Many women also went along to see the great event. Of course Mr. Meacham was there.

It was a colorful race. It looked as if a boom town had suddenly sprung up. Carriages, buggies, wagons, and men on horseback swarmed in. Many of the Indians came dressed in their fanciest costumes, although normally they wore clothes like the white people's. Now they lounged about in the few tall tepees that had been pitched. Their women, many with babies laced in papoose cases on their backs, guarded bundles of trade goods. Feather headdresses, mink- and seal-trimmed buckskin jackets, and beaded leggings and moccasins were displayed on buffalo robes spread on the ground.

The betting started. Stacks of twenty dollar gold pieces were wagered. Horses were bet against horses and they were tied together and put in the charge of Indian boys. Knives, pistols, saddles, even coats and hats and vests were placed as bets. Whatever the wager, it was tied to its mate and put aside to go to the winner after the race.

Two judges for the race were chosen—an Indian and a white man. Rivalry grew. More Indian goods were tied to the white man's articles and thrown in with the other bets.

Joe Crabb told his friends who had bet on his horse not to worry, that it was a sure thing. He had not only timed both horses, but the evening before, Joe whispered, the chief had been careless. He had allowed his pinto to be staked out a long way from camp where the grass was better. Joe slyly admitted that this mistake had been easy to use to his advantage. He told his friends how he had sent a man out to "borrow" the pinto, and leave another pinto in its place so it would not be missed. Then far out on the prairie, in the moonlight, he had raced the pinto against his own Kentucky horse. There was no doubt about it. Joe's Thoroughbred was much the faster horse. Then the chief's pinto was taken back to his stake rope to go on with his grazing, and no one was wiser. At least, that was what Joe thought.

Poker-faced Chief Howlish knew all about the switch and the trial race, for he had planned it that way. The pinto Joe had tried out was a look-alike half brother of the chief's number one racing pinto.

Joe's clever trick was whispered about among the white men. The race seemed a sure thing, so the Cayuse people were taunted into still more bets. Silk and satin vests were taken off and bet against buckskin beaded ones. Even a few wagons and carriages had Indian ponies tied to their wheels to show that they were wagered. The Cayuse people acted fearful and unsure, but even so they brought up more horses to gamble with.

When the betting was finished the race was called. The rival horses were brought to the starting line. The blanket came off Joe's sleek racer. He was an aristocrat from his quivering nostrils to his rounded quarters and muscled hind legs. All eyes were on the prancing animal as the wrinkle-faced jockey was boosted into the tiny racing saddle.

Then the pinto emerged from the crowd of Indians surrounding him. He seemed quiet and unconcerned. He was uncurried and his mussed-up

mane concealed the nice arch of his neck. What a poor showing he made at the side of the Thoroughbred!

At that moment the white men must have felt a twinge of conscience. How could the reds be foolish enough to wager so much on this range pony! Winning the race was like taking candy from a baby.

The chief waved to an Indian boy. The lad slipped his blanket off and in a light fluid motion leaped to the pinto's back. He had no saddle. His bridle was a thong about the pony's jaw. With this he neck-reined the pinto toward the starting place.

As the horse stepped out a startling change came over him. A moment before he had seemed like any herd pony; now he came to life and danced on springy legs.

During the first false starts the rippling muscles under his dirty hide sent the pinto whirling away. But he was easily turned and brought back by his young rider.

The Kentucky horse, on the other hand, was in a frenzy of excitement and difficult to control. He fretted and lunged. The chief was pleased to see the Kentucky horse tiring himself.

Some of the white men began to look a little worried. Why had they bet so heavily? Perhaps the race was not a sure thing after all.

When at last the race was on with a shouted "go," the racers were soon lost in a cloud of dust as they sped away toward the far turning post. The white men and the Indians shouted and cheered. The white men were wildly hopeful that Joe's horse would be ahead on the way back. But when the horses drew into sight and they saw the pinto out in front, their hopes were shattered. The Cayuse Indians had done it again. They had taken the white men—lock, stock, and barrel.

Mr. Meacham said the time for the race had been nine minutes and fifty-one seconds. If it is at all possible that he was correct, it was an amazing record for five miles. But whatever the time, the pinto had simply run away from the Kentucky horse. The jockey on Joe's horse pulled up and did not even try to finish the race when he saw how hopeless it was.

This was not a day the white men liked to talk about. The trick Joe had pulled to assure victory for the white men had backfired on them all.

Chief Howlish felt so good about winning the race, he played the part of a great-hearted prince. He gave back to Joe one of the horses he had won from him. Then he lent him some money. But he cautioned him about ever again stealing another man's horse to try him out.

He said good humoredly, "Joe, you not know how to make my horse run. Cla-hoy-um [Goodbye]."

Mr. Meacham said he thought the chief's pinto race horse was one-half Kentucky Thoroughbred. He recalled that years before, one of the emigrants to Oregon had brought a Thoroughbred stallion from Kentucky, which had fathered some running horses in the Umatilla country.

Chief Howlish was later offered five thousand dollars for the pinto. He refused to sell, saying that he didn't need the money.

It does seem certain the chief had plenty of money. He told Mr. Meacham he was willing to deposit forfeit money in an Oregon bank to pay the expenses of any eastern racing stable owner who would come to the West and match speed with his pinto in a five-mile race. "If my horse loses," Chief Howlish said, "the owner of the horse that wins can collect the forfeit money."

"In that event," Mr. Meacham wrote jokingly, "the eastern winner would also win enough Cayuse ponies to overload the Union Pacific Railroad."

Although Indians loved horse racing and had a lot of fun with the sport, an Indian warrior had three regular jobs that came before sport. The first was to hunt to feed his family. The second was to fight to defend his home, and to win fame and honor. The third was to steal horses to gain wealth. He stole horses not only from the Spaniards but from other tribesmen he considered his enemies. Horse stealing was an exciting incentive for carrying on the endless tribal warfare.

For each job the warrior had a special mount. Of the three, the war horse was usually his favorite. He might swap others but never his war horse. The fighting horses were fast but easily controlled. A fighting horse was often trained to drag its fallen rider from the field by letting the Indian cling to its tail. Straps were braided into the tail hairs so the warrior would have something to grasp. Loops were also braided in the horse's mane near the withers. From these loops the warrior could swing down beside the pony's neck and shoulder, using the pony as a shield so he could shoot arrows or bullets under its neck at his enemy.

The daring and skill of Indian riders was described by the famous mountain man Kit Carson and other frontiersmen who told of seeing Indians race into the midst of fighting to carry off their wounded. If a downed brave was still able to lift his arms, two of his friends would come sweeping by at a gallop, one on each side of the wounded man, and swinging down each would grab one of his arms and tear from the field with him suspended in the air between them.

Because Indians were with their best riding horses from morning until night almost every day, they had plenty of opportunity to train their ponies exactly to their liking. But to the white men some of the things they did to their horses seemed cruel and severe. At an early period, Indians slit the nostrils of their ponies, thinking this allowed the animals to breath in more air so they could run longer. Ear splitting, too, was a common practice. It was a way of marking or branding the horse and, to the Indian mind, an attractive touch of decoration. Sometimes the braves strapped deer or buffalo horns on the heads of their war horses to make them look ferocious. Or they might paint the horses' heads and tails a brilliant red.

Next to the war horse the Indian prized his buffalo-hunting horse. This one was trained for great endurance, for often the chase would go on for hours. In addition to good wind, the pony had to be bold and willing to run in close to the shaggy beasts, risking the lunges of the deadly horns.

Once at a county fair when I was a small boy, I saw an Indian on horseback chase a buffalo and kill it with an arrow. The buffalo was not very big, and he looked rather bewildered when he was turned loose at one end of the race track oval. When the Indian came dashing up—bareback on a pinto pony—the buffalo ran surprisingly fast. Once or twice he swung his head as if he meant to swerve to hook the horse. But the pony would dodge and then run in close again. Then, so quickly that we could hardly see it, the Indian drew back the arrow in his bow and shot. The arrow hit the beast behind the near shoulder. He ran for thirty or forty feet, then fell down dead. All of us felt sorry for the buffalo. In chasing a single beast, this Indian was taking very little risk. A much greater risk was taken when a hunter raced along on the edges of the big herds. His horse might step in a prairie dog hole and go down, or be hemmed in by the many running buffalo so that he could not dodge when the horns slashed at him. Many Indian hunters, in their efforts to get buffalo meat for their families, went to their deaths beneath the trampling hoofs.

In breaking horses to ride, Indians found, as do most horsemen, that the handling and training goes much easier if done when the animals are colts. If horses run wild until they are fully grown, the breaking can be difficult. One unique method used by the Indians to break wild horses was to drive them along with some tame horses into a pond or lake. The wild ones were unable to buck or strike out with their feet when packed in close with the others and in water that was up over their bellies. Indian boys would then leap from one pony to another. It was one of their favorite summertime sports. The wild ponies soon lost their fear, and from then on were easily handled and trained. Indians who had no water that was deep enough used other methods, some of them very cruel.

Until they learned from the cowboys who came along later, the Indians seldom broke a horse by letting him buck. Usually the wild pony was tied to a tree and starved for several days, even made to go without water. Very little fight was left in the animal when the time came for someone to get on his back. Blindfolds were also used. Blindfolded horses hesitate to make any violent moves for fear they will run into something.

Indian horse breakers would sometimes tie up a forefoot of the animal in such a way that the foot could be let down and pulled up again by the rider. The rider had little trouble getting on a three-legged horse. When the rider let the foot down and the horse started off, the foot could again be jerked up should the horse start to buck, and the pony would go tumbling to his knees. A few severe lessons in which his knees got hurt cured the pony of bucking.

The rig or tack Indians once used was very simple. For a bridle, a hair or leather rope was tied around the pony's lower jaw in the gap behind the bridle teeth so the pony could not bite it in two. The Indian saddle was often a crudely shaped wooden frame covered with rawhide. Because this kind of saddle seldom fitted well, it rubbed and scraped and caused sores. Indian ponies with bleeding backs were not uncommon, and only the most thoughtful Indians bothered to cover the wounds with mud or hides to keep off the blowflies and the magpies.

Bareback riding was the more usual custom, not so much because it spared the backs of the ponies, but because it reduced the chances of the rider getting hung up in the stirrups and being dragged, if thrown or knocked from the pony.

The warriors and hunters usually kept only a few favored mounts tethered on lariats, or hobbled, to graze close to camp. The rest of the horses, although privately owned, mingled in big common herds. There were no fenced pastures. A few young herdsmen kept an eye on the horses and if they wandered too far away they were driven back to the home range.

In the winter, the horses, like other wild animals, foraged for food as best they could. When snow covered the ground the horses cleared it away with their hoofs to get at the hay-like cured grass beneath. In the most severe weather, a few favorites, such as the war horses and the buffalo horses might be brought into the hogans or tepees to live with the family. Food was always scarce in winter for both people and horses. There were winters when the horses had nothing but cottonwood bark to eat, and they even chewed the wood when there was nothing else. With the coming of spring, people and horses were gaunt. Then, with good hunting weather the people ate well again and the succulent spring grass put flesh on the horses. The month of June had a special meaning for the Horse Indians. They called it "the month that horses get fat."

After owning horses for fifty or sixty years, many Plains tribes were stealing and raising more horses than they could possibly use. Grass was free and horses were wealth. It seemed better to have too many horses than too few. The more horses a warrior owned, the more he was looked up to by his family and tribesmen. Then, too, some might stray away or be stolen. It was well to have many, many horses, the warriors reasoned. So the horses increased in number and many were never used at all. Horses that are not tamed and handled go native. That is to say, all their feral, or wild instincts come back. Many unused animals left the herd to roam about and hunt for food and raise their young like other wild animals. Like their former owners, the roaming Indians, these wild horses lived in family groups. A strong, fierce fighting stallion would bring together a family of mares and colts. And, just like the Indians, the wild horses had their tribes or herds. But even when they ran with herds the stallion kept his own family together as a group. He was their protector, watching and sniffing, ready to warn his *manada,* or family, of any lurking wolves or mountain lions or grizzly bears.

When attacked, horses can fight with their teeth and flailing hoofs, but their best protection is their fleetness. Out on the oceanlike swells of the open prairies, no animal enemy can catch them. There, where nothing checks their running, it is very difficult, even for human enemies to round them up and capture them.

The Indian horses that escaped became freedom-loving mustangs and they were known by many names. Some men lumped all western horses under the name of "Indian Pony." Other men used the name *bronco* or *bronc*—a Spanish word meaning untamed or rough. In districts where the mustangs became small with heads too big for their bodies, they were given the uncomplimentary name of "hammerheads." Many mustangs got their tails matted with cockleburrs and these earned the name of "broomtails" or "fuzztails."

Whatever these horses were called, the men who knew them when they were at their best valued them for their quickness, sure-footedness, intelligence, and amazing endurance. In their veins ran the aristocratic blood of the marvelous horses bred by the old Spanish and Moorish knights.

To go back to the beginning of the mustang heards, it should be noted that the Mexicans, as well as the Horse Indians, raised more horses than they could tame and use. Horses from Mexican ranches wandered from their home pastures, seeking more and better grazing. Finally, thousands and thousands of them—ownerless and wild—moved north above the Rio Grande. Some stampeded across the river during Indian raids. Later on, American horses that came from east of the Mississippi River with the early settlers strayed away or were run off by marauding Indians. Many of these horses of English breeding joined the wild herds. With this new mixture, the mustangs were no longer of pure Spanish horse blood. The mustangs, like American people, became a blending of many races.

The first horses had come to America with Cortés in 1519. Following them, a race of highly cultured, horse aristocrats grew up on the Mexican ranches. Some three hundred and forty years later, the horses that roamed the western plains were no longer cared-for, cultured horses. They were ownerless horses—that had gone back to a feral state—they were the *mustangs.*

CHAPTER SEVEN

The Mustangers

The mustangs reached their greatest number between 1775–1850. Men who saw the immense herds remembered them as one of the wonders of the West.

Once, a company of Texas Rangers met a drove of mustangs so large that it took over an hour to pass them, although both the rangers and the mustangs were traveling at rapid speed and going in opposite directions. As far as the eye could see, a dense mass of horses covered the dead level of the prairie. John C. Duval, one of the rangers, wrote, "The trampling of their hooves sounded like the roar of the surf on a rocky coast."

One of the first white men to make a big business of capturing and selling mustangs was Philip Nolan. He was an adventurous, mysterious man, and not much is known about him.

When he was a boy in the frontier town of Frankfort, Kentucky, he was befriended, and perhaps even raised, by the equally mysterious General James Wilkinson. The general was accused, but never convicted, of promoting schemes to take over part of Texas from the Spanish and set himself up as ruler. It was rumored that Philip was on secret missions for his benefactor, when he made trips into that forbidden province. We do know that he brought back many mustangs from Texas.

Somehow, Thomas Jefferson, then Secretary of State, heard about Philip Nolan and the mustangs. Everything concerning the country west of the Mississippi River was of interest to Jefferson, and he wrote to Nolan asking about them. A man named Daniel Clark Jr., who worked for Nolan, answered, saying that Nolan was away on a trip to Texas.

Whether Nolan ever wrote to Jefferson about the wild horses is not known. It is known that Philip Nolan made several trips to Texas between 1790 and 1800. On one of his trips to the Rio Grande he purchased tame horses and mules from Mexican ranches. At other times he hired *mesteñeros,* or mustang hunters to work for him. All stock, Spanish horses and mules and mustangs, were taken to East Texas where Nolan had pastures, corrals, and cabins along the Trinity River. From there the herds went to his headquarters on the west bank of the Mississippi River, across from Natchez. When the stock was broken and put in good condition, it was sold to planters in the vicinity or sent to the markets of New Orleans.

The elegantly dressed, dashing Nolan was welcomed in the best society. Vague stories of his adventures among the Indians were passed along, and people wondered about his secretive trips into Spanish-held Texas. To the young ladies of New Orleans and Natchez, the mystery surrounding him made him appear even more handsome and romantic, and they were charmed by his gallant manners and fine dancing. The lovely Fanny Lintot became his bride, and their honeymoon was spent at the white-columned mansion "Concordia," the home of Fanny's relatives which was not far from Nolan's headquarters.

Only a few months after their marriage in 1799, Nolan went again on a journey to Texas. This time he took a well-armed party. Certain Spanish officials at the border gave or sold to Nolan the necessary entry permits.

We don't know whether or not Philip Nolan was true to his first name. The name "Philip" comes from the Greek and means horse lover. If he was a horse lover, he must have suffered great remorse over what happened to the last herd of mustangs he captured.

On this particular trip he traveled farther west than he ever had before. One day his party of mustangers met a Spanish patrol of fifty troopers. The officer in charge noticed the long rifles of the Americans and decided not to challenge their right to be in Texas, nor even ask to see their permit papers.

After that meeting the Nolan party journeyed west up the Red River and then turned south. Game was scarce so they lived on wild horse meat. Somewhere in the vicinity of present Waco, Texas, they saw big herds of mustangs. Camp was made and Nolan had his men build a cabin and a large corral. Out from the entrance to the corral they built long fences of brush and logs. The fences forved a v, so that when the mustangs were driven into this wide mouth they would be funneled through the narrow gate. When all was ready the men worked in relays to round up the mustangs. By keeping them from watering places and by having men always near the fringes of the herd, so that the mustangs could not rest, graze, or sleep, the riders gradually wore them down. With all men in the saddle for the big push, the tired mustangs were hazed into the funnel that led them through the gate. With a cheer of victory, the gate was closed on two hundred and fifty mustangs.

The cheers were hardly out of their mouths when the men saw a band of painted Indians riding up. They were Comanches. Their leader, stern and frowning, told Nolan, who had learned the Comanche language, that he and his men would have to come with him and parley with the big chief.

Nolan was a shrewd trader and he understood Indians. He was confident he could make a deal with the tribal leaders even though he and his small party were deep in Comanche country. He told his men to stay together and show no fear—and to keep their guns handy. All his men got on their horses and, leaving the corral unguarded, took their pack animals with them and followed the Indians. They had ridden most of the day before they entered a big tepee town, where the chief and his head men greeted them in a solemn, impressive manner. Food was brought and the tired, hungry men pitched in to eat, always keeping their guns within easy reach. The hospitable manner of the Indians told Nolan that everything would be done in the leisurely, ceremonial, Indian way.

After supper, Nolan ordered a pack animal unloaded, and to the delighted Indians who gathered around he passed out some beads and knives and shirts as a token of good will. Later, sitting in a circle in serious council, promises of opening regular trade were made. Nolan said he would bring more goods in exchange for more mustangs.

Indians love to parley. For them it is a form of entertainment, and they have many ways in which to prolong the meetings. During the next three days Nolan tried many times to end the visit so that he and his men could be on their way. Each time, the Indians stopped him and insisted they talk some more, or eat some more, or smoke some more. Nolan did not dare offend his unpredictable hosts. Throughout the meetings with the Indians, Nolan and his men had been worried about the mustangs locked up in the corral without food or water.

When they did manage to get away from the over-hospitable Comanches, they pushed their horses to the limit of endurance to get back to the corral. They were too late. Every one of the two hundred and fifty mustangs lay dead of thirst.

Early the next morning they heard the tramp of horses and the clink of arms. Rubbing their sleepy eyes the men looked to the priming of their rifles and waited. As dawn broke they saw that they were surrounded by Spanish troopers. Soon after, without a word being addressed to anyone in the cabin, the Spanish patrol opened fire.

The mustangers might have stood off the larger force of Spaniards, had it not been for the loss of their gallant leader. Within ten minutes after the start of the fight, Philip Nolan lay dead. A musket ball had hit him in the head. His men asked for a truce. During the short talk that followed, the mustangers were tricked into laying down their arms. Although none of them were ever formally tried and sentenced, all were taken as prisoners to the Zacatecas silver mines in Mexico, where they were forced to toil away their lives.

For many years to come, this land of the mustangs in the Southwest was to be a land of violence and conflict.

Mustangers had to be tough, patient, hard-riding, and cunning men. Sometimes they kept on the trail for days, waiting for a chance to run a band of mustangs into a "boxed" canyon (one that ends in steep unclimbable walls), where the animals could be cornered and roped. Some mustangers preferred to tire the wild horses, just as Nolan had done. Rope snares placed along the mustang trails that led to water were occasionally successful.

Some mustangers who were crack shots with a rifle tried what they called "creasing." The point was to send a bullet through the top of the animal's neck. It was a risky and cruel way of knocking a mustang down. If the bullet hit too low it killed the horse, and if the shot missed, the frightened animal would run out of sight. But if the bullet just clipped the cartilage in the horse's neck near the head, the horse would fall to the ground stunned, and remain down long enough to be tied by the neck or to have his forefeet hobbled.

After wild horses were caught, there were several ways of controlling them. One way was to tie two of them together by the neck. One horse couldn't decide to run or turn or dodge just when the other wanted to. They jerked each other around so roughly that both horses learned to move slowly. Beside having their feet hobbled, some mustangs were forced to drag logs at the end of neck ropes.

The most gentle of all ways to catch mustangs was to rope them when they were colts. A colt lagging behind an escaping herd sometimes would come within range of a roper's noose. The captured colt was nursed by a tame mare in camp or fed on cow's milk. It wasn't long before he was a pet, as gentle as any barnyard pony.

Whatever the method used, it was never easy to capture mustangs. As well as being constantly alert, the horses often had "sentinels" on guard. While the mustangs grazed, blackbirds sat on their necks picking insects from their manes. When the blackbirds took fright and flew away, the mustangs were warned of danger. The father of the family, the stallion tried to find higher ground for a lookout on which to graze. There he ate in fits and starts. Nervously, his head would swing up to check on his band and to see if the buffalo and antelope herds were showing signs of uneasiness.

The mustang herds were made up of many *manadas*. *Manada* is a Spanish word, as are so many words dealing with the ranching business in the Southwest. Each *manada* had from three to twenty mares with colts of varying ages. The *manadas* might wander far from the main herd to graze, but the mustangs in each family stayed close together. The ruling stallion saw that they did. He was very jealous and full of fight. Each spring he had to fight off the younger stallions who tried to steal mares with which to start *manadas* of their own. With mouth wide open, the screaming older stallion would charge into bloody, biting, hide-slashing combat with the challenger. If whipped and driven off, the crestfallen younger stallion, without any mares of his own, would rejoin his bachelor friends. A rancher once told me he saw twenty or more stallions in one bunch. All, he said, seemed fairly young.

If the old stallion was beaten in the fight with a younger one, he nearly always died soon after from wounds. If he did live, he would wander off alone or stray along with a buffalo herd for protection. Seldom would the injured pride of a deposed mustang monarch allow him to live again in the horse herds.

When a *manada* broke into a run from fright or just for the fun of it, the stallion did not go to the front to lead them. That job was taken over by one of the smart, fast mares. The stallion, the lord and master, ran alongside or circled the rear, forcing the stragglers to keep up.

In our town of Woodward, a special hero of mine ran a small hotel. He was called Dad Nall by everyone. Never just Dad, but always Dadnall, pronounced as if it were one word.

He lived during the days of the Indian campaigns, the longhorn trails, the mining booms, and the cattle wars. He had done about everything that had to be done in the West, and now he was an hotel owner.

On my way home from school I used to stop by to sit in the little lobby and ask him about the things he had done and seen. Usually something would remind him of a story to tell me. One bitterly cold day I stopped in to get out of the icy wind. Dad Nall watched me get close to the big stove as I cupped my hands around my cold ears.

"Reminds me," he said, as he leaned contentedly on the counter, "of the winter I worked for the Turkey Track outfit in Texas. That was one of the worst winters that ever hit the Panhandle. In such flat country there was nothing between it and the North Pole to stop a blizzard from swooping along, but a few barbed-wire fences. Our boots were almost frozen to the stirrups when we got in one evening. One of the boys didn't get in till plumb dark. He came stomping into the bunk house and took off his hat that he'd tied on with a bandanna handkerchief, and got up close to the stove. He made a big mistake in trying to thaw out too fast. He rubbed his ears—just like you're doing—and danged if they didn't come clean off."

My hands came away from my ears as I leaped away from the stove. Ever since then, I have remembered to thaw out slowly!

On one occasion Dad Nall told me how he had come almost face-to-face with a beautiful mustang stallion. While out hunting strays along the South Canadian River in the Panhandle, he came over a ridge and saw a bunch of mustang mares and colts. Off to one side, and nearer to him, was the startled stallion. Dad Nall must have been down wind to get so close, because mustangs have keen senses of smell.

Dad Nall said the stallion was a Palomino, the color of gold with a cream-colored mane and tail. For a moment man and horse just looked at each other. Then the Palomino jumped, ran a short distance, and whirled around to give the intruder a good looking over. Head high, nostrils distended, he looked angry, proud, and disdainful. Snorting, he pointed his ears at Dad Nall, studying him, gauging the danger. The Palomino's sleek coat glistened with each slight movement. He half reared, then pawed the ground a few times with a forefoot. In horse talk he was saying, "Stay where you are, you've come close enough."

Suddenly with a shrill neigh he wheeled and pounded back to the bunch of mares and their foals. Every gesture, every wave of his angry head with his ears laid back, told the mares to quit dawdling and get going. None questioned their king and leader. The mustangs all broke into a run, while the stallion circled the laggards, handling the racing band as if it were a retreating army and he a fierce general.

Thinking that he might have some luck and rope a colt, Dad Nall said he galloped along in the mustangs' wake of dust. One of the colts began to tire and it and its mother lagged farther and farther behind. The stallion circled back and rushed at the mare with a vicious, almost human shriek, forcing her and the colt to catch up with the herd. Again the colt slowed down. He simply couldn't keep up.

Dad Nall ran out a loop in his lariat. It looked as if he might get a colt after all. But the stallion saw what was happening, and with white teeth flashing, the big Palomino ran at the colt. One swift bite in the back of the head killed it. The helpless and resigned mare was driven forward with the others by the raging stallion.

Dad Nall said he lost sight of the bunch as they ran through a gap in the hills, swallowed up in a cloud of dust.

Wild leaders like this golden Palomino were seldom caught and tamed. Some would kill—even themselves—rather than be captured. Once, far up the Cimarron River near Black Mesa, a magnificent dark bay stallion with a white-starred forehead, got trapped on a mesa ledge. Rather than submit to the ropers who were closing in on him, he committed suicide. With head up and mane flying he leaped far out into the air to fall to his death in the valley below.

Around their evening cooking fires, the Mexican *mesteñeros* and the American mustangers would talk about the magnificent stallions they had seen or caught or almost caught. Like fish stories, it seemed the best ones always got away. Facts became blended with legends. Fleeing mustang stallions ran on and on into a land bounded only by memories, where the mus-

tang immortals roamed—Black Devil, Red Devil, The Golden Dun, the White Steed of the Prairies, The Pacing White Stallion, the Ghost Horse, The Phantom White Stallion, Star Face of the Cimarron breaks, and many others.

No matter how many legendary mustangs led men on fruitless quests, it is a fact that untold thousands—even millions—of mustangs, some times including even the elusive stallions, were captured and taught to behave as all good, civilized ponies should.

One mustang king that lured men on with the dream of capturing him was, strangely, a Kentucky Thoroughbred that had been run off from a settlement in Kansas by Cheyenne warriors. After escaping from the Indians, the horse was seen running with his own band of mustang mares. Every mustanger and range rider who got a glimpse of the beautiful stallion wanted to capture him. His flowing mane and tail, his arched neck and proud carriage made the horse look much larger than he was. He was as black as a crow's wing and was given the name of Black Kettle, for the noted Cheyenne chief. For years men tried to run him down, walk him down, keep him from water, grass, and rest, and wear him down. And of course they tried to rope or trap him, but all attempts were unsuccessful—which made men want him all the more.

One young mustanger named Frank Lockard, and his partner William Simpson of Norton, Kansas, became so enthralled with the dream of capturing Black Kettle, that they spent most of their time trailing him. Days followed into weeks and months into years and still Black Kettle led them a merry chase.

While Simpson carried on what was left of their horse business, Frank Lockard stayed on the trail. He ran down his good saddle horses. Several times he lost his way, and once he almost froze to death. On one wild chase, led of course by Black Kettle, Lockard drove a team hitched to a buckboard over the open prairie for thirty miles without stopping. By the time he stopped, the team was wind-broken and ruined.

But Frank was a man who wouldn't give up, and at last the day came when he drove the exhausted Black Kettle, along with a few other tired mustangs into a small corral. It was evening and he was almost as tired as the stallion, but he was so eager to try out the famous "Monarch of the Prairies" that he threw a saddle on him then and there and rode him. To Frank's surprise the great Black Kettle was not difficult to master and tame.

For a while Frank basked in the limelight, as all eyes turned to stare at him and the renowned mustang he often rode down the main street of Norton. But except for his fame, Black Kettle turned out to be no more desirable than many other horses. Then a skin disease caused his beautiful mane and tail to become scraggly. After a time the name Black Kettle lost its magic and Frank sold him. The once proud stallion that had eluded so many men to keep his freedom wound up pulling a milk wagon.

Mabry (Mayberry) Gray, a young Texan, once captured a mustang stallion in a hurry, in order to save his own life. Like so many other stories of the mustangs, this one was tracked down by Professor J. Frank Dobie of Texas, who, through the years, rounded up many "old timers" and curried and combed the accumulated error from their wild yarns. He corraled more lore of the mustangs and the longhorns than any writer I know.

Mabry Gray, a tall, lanky southerner, was once far out on the Texas plains hunting buffalo with some friends. He was galloping alongside a herd of buffalo when his horse stumbled and fell with him, just at the instant he shot a buffalo. Mabry fell sprawling on the ground close to the buffalo he had just killed. His pony, badly frightened by the herd that thundered by, got up, jerked away and ran off. Luckily Mabry was not hurt. For hours he wandered afoot in search of his horse or his companions, who not seeing his accident, had raced on following the buffalo.

At last hunger forced him to return to the buffalo he had shot. He built a small fire, roasted some of the buffalo meat and ate it, then walked to a clump of trees that bordered a small pool, where he quenched his thirst. There in the shade he rested and pondered his predicament. If he attempted to walk back to the settlement across the hot prairie he would die of thirst, he reasoned. His only chance of survival was to catch a mustang and tame him enough to ride him.

Horse tracks told him that mustangs came to the pool to drink. So, in order to be out of sight when they came that evening, he climbed a tree. Sure enough, the horses came, and from a limb that hung out over the water Gray quietly watched the fine looking animals wading into the pond.

His thoughts were on the problem of how to catch one. If he only had a rope! Then a plan began forming in his mind, and with it came hope. As soon as the mustangs wandered away, he hurried down from his perch and went to the dead buffalo. First he skinned the beast, and then he cut the hide into strips. With these hairy strips he started to plait a lariat and went on working until it was too dark to see. For two days he worked on the long lariat, and also on an extra length for a belly band or surcingle. When the leather ropes were finished, he rubbed them with buffalo fat to keep them pliable. Before the horses came in that evening, he was ready.

With one end of the lariat tied to the tree, and the loop end in his hand, he crawled out on the big limb, in position to throw. He knew he must not miss. If the mustangs were frightened they might not return to the pool. After a short wait, he saw the horses coming, playfully snapping at each other and kicking up their heels. The mares waded into the pool and swished their noses in the water to clear the surface of scum. Above them crouched Mabry as quiet as a puma about to spring. He was not going to be choosy— he would try and rope the mustang that made the best target for his noose.

While he watched the bay stallion, the ruler of the band, came closer than any of the others. Holding his breath, Mabry waited tensely for the horse to move his head into a better position for the throw. Perhaps his arm brushed a limb, or perhaps Mabry's scent was wafted down, but something caused the bay's head to come up as he whirled with explosive suddenness. The noose flew down, encircling the bay's neck. Mabry had him! He clung tightly to his tree limb, bracing against the impact he knew would come. When the stallion hit the end of the rope, the tree quaked as the horse was jerked to the ground with a terrific thud. The next instant he was on his feet again, striking out and lunging against the lariat, fighting the strange foe that gripped him by the throat. His *manada* went racing away in fright.

Mabry climbed down from the tree, and stood for a while looking at his catch. Then he started talking to the struggling stallion as he walked slowly toward him, while grasping the lariat. The stallion's fear of what Mabry would do to him brought on a spasm of flailing forefeet and violently jerking head. Mabry leaped back and waited. Then he tried again, his voice easy, soothing, monotonous. The stallion was still snorting defiance when Mabry called off the taming for the night.

The next morning Mabry got close enough to reach out and try to touch the stallion's head. Again the terrified animal made a frantic effort to break the lariat, succeeding only in pulling the noose more tightly around his throat. But as the hours passed the choking horse gradually fought less, and at last Mabry was able to grasp the noose and ease it. With more air to breathe the horse grew quieter, allowing Mabry to make a hackamore, or halter, with the lariat.

Now when the animal pulled back, the pressure was on his nose instead of his throat. Firmly grasping the hackamore close to the horse's jaw—to keep him from turning and striking with either hind feet or forefeet—Mabry eased an arm over the animal's back. He did this many times, talking and gently patting the stallion while he put as much weight as he could on his back, and jumping away when the horse became too violent to hold. Both the man and the horse were desperately tired, but it was the man who had the stronger will to win. Carefully he tied the leather surcingle around the stallion's body and then, with a quick leap, was on the mustang's back, holding on to the surcingle. The first bucking lunges headed them both for the trees. Then with a swerve the bay bucked out to the end of the lariat. It was still tied to the tree and it jerked the horse around so fast that Mabry went sailing off, to land, luckily, unharmed.

After calming the bay down, Mabry got ready to ride again. This time he blindfolded the horse with his bandanna handkerchief. He strapped his rifle on his own back, walked over and untied the lariat from the tree and coiled it. He had blindfolded the stallion because he knew it would be easier to mount if the horse couldn't see what was going on. Quickly he grasped the surcingle and jumped on the stallion's back, then leaned forward and jerked the blind from the horse's eyes.

The stallion lunged for the sky, as Mabry hauled on his head, forcing him out of a series of pitching jumps into a run. The horse was greatly fatigued and confused by all that had happened to him, but being a Spanish mustang he had a remarkable reserve of endurance. He ran for miles. Mabry did not spare him. Only when the animal was stumbling from exhaustion did Mabry dismount. Both he and the horse were ready for some rest. While the mustang, tied to a mesquite bush, got his breath and began to graze, Mabry ate some of the cooked buffalo meat he had brought in his pockets and then went to sleep.

By daylight he was again on the back of the mustang, covering the prairie miles. Often during the next two days he stopped so that he and his mount could rest and get a bite to eat. It was quite by accident that he found his friends where they had made camp for the night. They had given up all hope of ever finding him. For the rest of his life Mabry Gray was known in that part of Texas as Mustang Gray.

Of all the ways to catch mustangs the most foolhardy, it seemed, was simply to race alongside and leap upon a mustang's back. Such a sight of acrobatic action was witnessed and reported by the late Jack Thorp, a polo-playing horseman from Long Island, New York, who went to New Mexico in the 1890's to become a cowboy and cattleman. In his later years he was a writer and collector of lore of the saddlemen of the Southwest.

Once when Thorp and some of his cowboy friends were riding in West Texas, they saw a herd of mustangs running toward them at an angle. As they watched they noticed that two *mesteñeros* were riding at great speed along the fringe of the herd, and crowding in close to the running mustangs. To their amazement, the cowboys saw the smaller of the two mustang hunters leap from a big white horse to the back of a sorrel mustang mare. The wild sorrel with the daring rider now clinging to its mane soon disappeared in the dust cloud that hovered over the racing mustangs. The big white horse, now without its rider, was caught by the other *mesteñero,* who slowed down and turned back. Leading the white horse he rode over to talk to Thorp and his friends.

They saw that he was a Mexican boy. It was his sister, he said, who had just leaped on the back of the wild sorrel mustang. He seemed unworried, saying that he was sure she would soon return safely with the captured animal. And, sure enough, in about thirty minutes the sister of the Mexican boy came riding toward them. The wild sorrel she rode was lathered with sweat and was subdued. The small girl, as they found out later, was fourteen years old. In answer to the cowboys' questions, she told them how she handled the mustang after she made the jump. A noose in a hair rope she carried was tossed over the sorrel's head and then, riding low over the neck, she flipped two half hitches over the mare's nose. By pulling on this makeshift hackamore she was able to turn the wild mare out of the herd.

The cowboys rode along with the young *mesteñera* and her *mesteñero* brother to the camp of their parents. There they met the father and mother and two younger sisters. They learned that both the father and mother had caught mustangs by making the wild leaps when they were younger. The father had broken both arms and both legs at different times, but he was still active and a good horse tamer. The son had gotten too heavy to make the

jumps, but the two younger sisters were already practicing the leaps on gentle horses so they too could one day try it on the mustangs. The horses the Mexicans used for the chase were of pure Spanish blood and were unusually tall for that breed—about sixteen hands high. When they had caught and broken twenty-five or thirty mustangs, the family said they would return with their horses to their home in Chihuahua, Mexico, for the winter.

CHAPTER EIGHT

The Mustang and the Indian Wa

The rush of American settlers to the West in the 1840's was the beginning of a mass migration that is still going on. The Indians, whose
homelands and hunting grounds were being overrun, fought to stop the
advancing tide. The conflict flared up off and on for over thirty years between two races of people with vastly different cultures. The Indians were
just emerging from the Stone Age, many of them still using flint arrowheads.
The white Americans, just entering the machine age, had industry, organiza-
tion, and equipment that made eventual victory certain. But in one respect
the white man had no advantage. Both races were still using the same
ancient, well-proven war weapon—the horse.

Without horses, the Indians would never have held off the white con-
querors as long as they did. Although more white people than Indians met
violent deaths in the raids and counterraids that ravaged the frontier, there
were more whites to take their places, and more kept pushing West. Indian
tribes could not organize and band together and form large armies because
their hunting grounds could not supply enough game to feed a dense popu-
lation. The warring Indians had no farms or supply centers. They had no

industry that could make a gun or gunpowder or even a knife. So the Indians carried on the only kind of warfare they could; a horseman's war in which small war parties made swooping, deadly attacks and rapid retreats.

In raids on wagon trains and settlements, many white people met with atrocious deaths and many women and children were dragged off by Indians as captives. If the infuriated pioneers, rangers, and soldiers who went in pursuit of the guilty Indians caught them, the vengeance of the white men at times matched in barbarity that of the Indians. More than once, unfortunately, United States frontier troops charged into the tepee towns of peaceful Indians by mistake. Hearing of innocent Indians being punished for the actions of a few bands of marauding Indians caused nearly all the Plains tribes to distrust and fear the white men, and to become more desperate in their struggle to survive.

More United States Army posts were set up to guard the settlements and overland trails, but the West is big and it was impossible to predict where the fast-traveling Indians would next strike. Because the horse was the Indian's best weapon, the United States Military Command decided the only way to quiet the frontier was to "un-horse" the Indian. As a result of this decision, many thousands of Indian ponies were slaughtered.

When I was a boy there were several old men living in our town who had taken part in the campaigns against the Indians. One of them was a Captain Tatlow who told me about his service with General George A. Custer's troops at a time when several hundred Indian ponies were rounded up and killed. As a very young man, Tatlow had served in the last year of the Civil War as a drummer boy. When the war ended, he joined a troop of the 7th Cavalry and was stationed at Camp Supply in Indian Territory. In the fall of 1868, General Custer, who had recently arrived to take command, received orders from his departmental commander, General Philip

Sheridan, which read: "Proceed in the direction of the Antelope Hills, thence toward the Washita River, the supposed winter seat of the hostile tribes; destroy their villages and ponies . . ."

My friend told about riding with the 7th Cavalry to carry out this mission. The object was to punish the Cheyennes for a murderous foray one of their war parties had made through western Kansas. They had killed many white settlers, and had taken two white women as captives. During that year more than eight hundred white men, women, and children had been killed on the frontier.

Custer's army marched south from Camp Supply in wintry November weather and on the fourth day out passed close to the Antelope Hills. Late in the evening of that day, Little Beaver and Hardrope, Osage Indian scouts attached to Custer's forces, reported to Custer that they had been far forward where they smelled cooking fires and they were certain that they had located the Cheyenne camp. With great caution the column marched on during the night. Every saddle squeak or clink of sabre or carbine seemed to shatter the stillness. Nerves were tense and the troopers whispered curses when their tired horses stumbled in the snow. Occasional halts were made to wait for reports from the scouts. At one halt orders came down the line for the force to divide into four detachments and to make a wide circuit of the village until it was completely surrounded.

Off in the darkness the riders dimly saw a black mass in a snowy valley. It was an immense pony herd. Young Tatlow, who was a Corporal at the time, was halted with his troop on the brow of a low hill. Below lay a cluster of pointed tepees spread out along the bank of the shallow Washita River.

Custer's plan was to attack as soon as it was light enough for his troopers to distinguish each other, yet early enough to surprise the sleeping village.

In gruff whispers the order was passed along the line for everyone to dismount and to be quiet about it. Then came the order for each trooper to put his fingers in his horse's mouth by the bit. This was done so that each man could tell instantly if his horse was going to whinny, and thus prevent it. My friend told me how he and the others danced and jigged in the snow during that bitterly cold dawn, to keep their feet from freezing, while hanging on to their horses' mouths.

At first light the troop commanders gave whispered orders to examine weapons, check cinches and to mount. This done, the troopers sat silent and waiting. Then it came—the band struck up the tune "Gary Owen," which was the signal to charge.

What followed is recorded in history books as the Battle of the Washita. Captain Tatlow, in telling about it almost fifty years later, said it was a massacre. Ironically, Custer had hit the camp of Black Kettle's peaceable Cheyennes. The Cheyenne war party he sought was camped farther down the stream. This was the second time that Black Kettle's people had been unjustly attacked by United States troops. Black Kettle had kept most of his Cheyennes off the warpath, not because he loved the white men, but because he saw the futility of fighting them.

Black Kettle and his wife rushed from their big buffalo-hide tepee and, with guns in hand, were among the first to fall. About fifty warriors were killed and almost that many women and children. Fifty-three Indian women and children were taken prisoner. Among the dead, three white captives were found, an unidentified little boy and a Mrs. Blinn and her child who had been taken by Indians a few months before in Colorado. The fact that the bodies of white captives were found justified the attack in the eyes of many people at the time.

Even though caught off guard and sound asleep when the shooting started, the Cheyennes fought with great courage, some refusing to retreat in the face of overwhelming odds, in order to give their families time to escape.

Before ten o'clock that morning the fighting was over. But to the surprise of the weary troopers more warriors were seen riding towards them up the valley. From a captured squaw, Custer learned that there were several more villages farther downstream. Warriors from these villages would have arrived sooner had they not been delayed by one of the 7th Cavalry's most beloved officers, Major Joel Elliott. This handsome young officer and fourteen of his men were pursuing a band of retreating braves downstream, when they encountered fresh warriors coming up from the lower villages. Soon

they were engulfed. Major Elliott and all his men were killed. Fearing that he would be outnumbered by the approaching warriors from downstream, Custer ordered his army to close ranks and start a retreat back to Camp Supply. He did not stay to find out what had happened to Major Elliott and his men.

So ended the battle of the Washita. General Sheridan's orders had been carried out. The morning's work had cost the 7th Cavalry twenty-one dead and fourteen wounded. An Indian village—the wrong one—had been destroyed with many of its people and eight hundred or more Indian ponies had been destroyed.

Captain Tatlow said he was thankful that his particular troop had not been detailed to "un-horse" the Indians, a job that took place as soon as the fighting ended. But he said he did recall seeing the ponies bunched together between two snowy hills and hearing the thudding clatter of the carbines as the troopers fired round after round into the herd. When the horrible noise stopped and the troopers rode away there was left an enormous red blotch covering acres in the snow.

Six years later, in 1874, fourteen hundred Kiowa horses met with the same fate. Colonel Ronald McKenzie, who had shown bravery and cool-headed leadership in frontier warfare, was sent with his 4th Cavalry and four companies of infantry to find and punish a desperate band of marauding Kiowas led by Chief Lone Wolf.

After many days of marching the colonel's scouts came upon the awesome depths of the Palo Duro (Hard Wood) Canyon. Sheer walls dropped to a stream that cut through a green valley far below, and nestled among the dark cedars were the white tepees of Lone Wolf's encampment.

Early the next morning a detachment started down a zigzag trail hoping to reach the valley floor before they were discovered. A lone Indian saw the troopers and fired, giving the alarm. One of the soldiers with accurate aim cut the Indian down instantly, little knowing that he was ending the life of Red Warbonnet, a famous Indian horseman. Red Warbonnet had gotten up early that morning, as usual, to take a look at his herd of beautiful white horses, of which he was justly proud.

In the running fight that followed the alarm, many of the Kiowa horses were left behind. It was reported that fourteen hundred head were captured by McKenzie's men and taken to nearby Tule Canyon and destroyed.

It is assumed that most of Red Warbonnet's white horses escaped along with other prized horses of the Kiowas, because for years following this battle, men told of having seen well-built, silvery sheened horses in mustang herds not far from the Palo Duro.

In 1876 at the battle of the Little Bighorn, in Montana, the Indians— mostly Sioux and Cheyenne under the leadership of Crazy Horse, Gall, and other chiefs used cavalry in a new and unheard-of way. The United States frontier troops were faced with the greatest gathering of Indian warriors that ever assembled on the North American Continent. At a crucial moment in the fighting hundreds of Indian riders were ordered to race back and forth in front of Major Reno's oncoming troopers. Such a cloud of dust was raised the Indians were enabled to shift their forces, unseen, to better ground. Reno's soldiers were defeated and driven back across the Little Bighorn River, where they were pinned down, unable to help the vain-glorious General Custer, whose detachment four miles downstream was surrounded and killed to a man, a few hours later.

This was probably the first time a full scale dust screen was used. Thirty-eight years later, in World War I, smoke screens were a much used device to conceal the movements of troops as they took new positions.

CHAPTER NINE

The Mustang Becomes the Cow Pony

The Southwest was the original home of the mustangs. It was also the home of the Spanish, or Mexican longhorn cattle. The first cattlemen in south Texas, the Mexicans, were excellent ranchers in some ways, but they never found a good market for their cattle. They raised more beef than they could sell or use, so, like the mustangs, the longhorns went on multiplying until they ranged far from their home pastures to become wild and ownerless.

Following the Civil War, a big market in beef opened up when railroads pushing into Kansas and Nebraska offered a way to get Western cattle to the Eastern markets. The millions of people pouring in from Europe to man the newly established industries in the East needed meat. Army posts in the West had to be supplied with beef, and Indians forced onto reservations by the United States Government had to be fed for a time by the Indian agencies.

All a pioneer rancher had to do to get into the cattle business was to go to Texas. There, he could find everything that was needed; ownerless wild cattle, an immense range of free grass almost cleared of Indians and

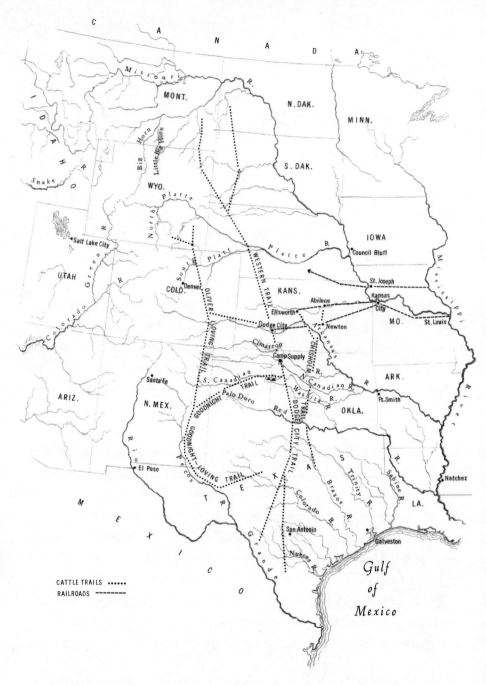

Chief herd trails over which Spanish horses and longhorn cattle traveled and early railroads that served the cattle shipping towns.

buffalo, and mustangs with which to handle the cattle. All three were waiting for men who were bold enough to go in and take them, men who could master the wild horses and wild cattle and hold part of the range in a wild country.

The history of the West was made by that kind of man. Riding half-tamed mustangs, the pioneer ranchers rounded up the wild longhorns in Texas and started the era of the long drives—trail-herding their cattle to the markets that opened up in Kansas towns along the new railroads. In boom towns such as Abilene, Ellsworth, and Dodge City, amid the bellow of steers and the whoop and holler of cowboys fresh off the long trails, cattle became big business. Whole herds were purchased at a time, to be shipped to markets farther east. Other herds of longhorns were trail-herded north by the thousands to stock the ranches that spread over the vast grasslands east of the Rocky Mountains. Wherever the longhorns went, it was the mustangs that took them; mustangs that had become cow ponies.

In those pioneering days the cattlemen were fortunate in having hardy native stock like the longhorns and the mustangs. The longhorns had hard hoofs and could stand up to the long trail drives. They could go without water twice as long as the more highly bred Herefords that came later. Out on the open range their long sharp horns protected them from the lobo wolves.

The mustangs, also, could travel long stretches between watering places. No other breed of horse had such hard hoofs and teeth, or such staying power under the saddle. No other breed could keep as strong or in as good flesh on a diet of grass alone. Most other horses soon wore down under hard work if they got no grain. Another very valuable quality possessed by the Spanish-blooded mustangs was an inborn aptitude for mastering and controlling cattle, a knack generally called cow sense.

It took only fifteen years for the great ranches of the West to be established. By 1880, with railroads forking into every part of the cattle country, the long drives to the railroad towns of Kansas were ending. No longer was the rangy, heavy-boned tough-meated, hard-footed and spear headed longhorn needed for hundreds of miles of travel. Now beef cattle could be improved.

Gradually the longhorns were replaced by the chunky, short-legged Herefords (white faces), Durhams, and Angus, imported from England and Scotland; cattle that carried more tender meat on their frames.

The saddle stock also was upgraded. Mustang mares were mated with blooded stallions whose lineage traced back to the quarter mile running horses of colonial days. The resulting offspring were called Quarter Horses. They became the most favored of all cowhorses. In this land of horsemen great pains were taken to keep records and to select outstanding sires and dams. Aristocratic sires such as Steel Dust, Shilo, Copperbottom, Printer, Traveler, and later Peter McCue, Zantanon, Joe Bailey, Old Sorrel, and others founded Quarter Horse families from which come today's show and short race winners.

In 1940 The American Quarter Horse Association, along with a registry of acceptable horses, was founded in Texas, thereby establishing a recognized breed—the Quarter Horse.

Quarter Horses have characteristics that are to be found in no other breed. They have cow-sense; an inborn ability to control cattle. They are level headed and calm and in contrast to other hot blooded fast running horses they quiet down quickly after fast and violent action. Cow horses have to turn bursts of speed on and off for hours at a time when working with cattle, so it is a great advantage if the horse can control himself and rest whenever there is a lull in the action.

From their mustang ancestors Quarter Horses inherited smartness, toughness, good wind, hard teeth and hoofs, and self-control. From their Thoroughbred, quarter-mile running ancestors they got blazing speed on the take-off, greater height, pliable sweet dispositions, and powerful driving muscles.

Today's modern ranches have been automated in much the same way as industry has been. Squeeze chutes and other devices to hold cattle while they are branded, injected, operated on, or dehorned, are in use. On some of the larger ranches jeeps and airplanes are used to inspect herds. But even with automation, the cow pony is still needed. Some pastures are too mountainous or brushy, or too broken by ravines for the use of jeeps. Airplanes are useful only for general inspection. For close observation of the condition of cattle a cowman has to ride into the herds on horseback. Cutting cattle from one herd into another is still necessary on the majority of ranches. Even roping stock is occasionally necessary.

It seems that plenty of work awaits the good cow pony.

There are slow ways and quick ways of taming and training cow ponies and other Western riding horses. In between these very different methods are others as varied as are the temperaments of men and horses.

The slow and gentle way is for the patient, easygoing person who has time, and can start with a colt when it is only a few months old. Daily handling and patting causes the colt to lose all fear of his trainer, and people generally, and since he is small a colt can't put up much resistance. Soon he is following naturally at the end of a halter rope. He stands quietly when his feet are picked up, and he playfully nuzzles his trainer as any pet would when he feels happy and at ease.

As the months go by, the colt is frequently caught up from pasture and handled and led about so that he won't forget his early lessons or develop any fear of his teacher. When he is going on three years old, he might be saddled and allowed to wear the saddle around in the corral until he gets used to it. He might even be driven with reins, held by someone walking behind him. He goes along with each new stunt without much fuss. When he is ridden for the first time, he takes that in stride too. Since he is not mad at anybody, he doesn't, as a rule, even try to buck.

A good horse trainer always stops each lesson before the pony gets tired. A tired pony can't learn. The training goes on week after week and when the colt has learned his latest lesson thoroughly, something new is added. He is taught to stand while his rider mounts, to neck rein, to back up, to step off into an easy canter or lope, to make quick, sliding stops, and to stand ground tied, when the reins are dropped to the ground. Horses learn by doing things over and over again. They are not the smartest of animals. Porpoises, elephants, apes, seals, and dogs have more reasoning ability. But once trained, a horse has a good memory and is dependable. And generally, horses have nice dispositions. They are not nearly as obvious about it as dogs, but when they trust a person they do want to please and be liked.

When, after many attempts, the pony goes through a new lesson quickly and smoothly, the trainer calls it a day. It is always well to end the session on a successful and happy note.

Before the pony is four years old he is working as a cow pony. If he has Spanish horse blood in him, as do all Quarter Horses, his natural-born cow sense, or cow savvy, will help him with his job from the start.

A sharp contrast to the slow and easy type of trainer is the horse breaker who is either pressed for time, or who doesn't believe in coddling horses. He starts work on horses that are full-grown—perhaps four or five years old—just as men did in the days of the mustangs. Some horsemen think that colts that have it too soft in the beginning lack the tough fiber and spirit of the horses that learn the hard and direct way.

Men who want to get the rough-and-tumble of breaking over with, will at the first lesson, "ride 'im out." This is the crudest and most extreme breaking method, and it calls for an expert bronc buster. The whole performance is a tussle from start to finish. After roping the animal, it takes two strong men to hold him while the saddle is being thrown on and cinched. One of the men will sometimes grab the bronc by the ear, put the tip of it in his own mouth, and clamp down on it with his teeth. The animal is so distracted that he stands as if paralyzed. When the rider is well seated in the saddle, the bronc is turned loose to explode into action. If the rider is still in the saddle when the horse "breaks in two"—cowboy slang for the moment when a bronco quits bucking and starts to run—the rider lets the horse race on until he is so tired he can be managed.

After three or four such workouts, the pony is started on the routine job of following cattle. Usually a hackamore is used instead of a bridle at first, while the pony is being taught to neck rein and to do all the other things cow ponies have to learn. For a number of days or weeks the rider must be on the alert. He is sitting on dynamite that might go off at any moment.

My father insisted that the mustangs be handled gently—at least as gently as possible. After a mustang was roped in a corral, the lariat was handed to a man on a big, solid saddle horse, who, with dallies of the rope about the saddle horn, helped to control the fighting animal. The big horse seemed to reduce the mustang's fear and to quiet him. While being held up close in a corner, the bronc was fitted with a combination hackamore and bridle with a snaffle or straight bit, and a saddle. Reins from the bit were buckled to the sides of the saddle so the pony's head could swing only slightly to either side. Trussed up in this fashion the pony was turned loose in the corral to get accustomed to a saddle and bridle.

If the fight went out of the pony fast, he was ridden after his second or third lesson, while being led by a man on horseback. With his head held close to the other horse, the bronc was unable to do more than lunge and jump around, so that any of us boys in our teens could easily stay in the saddle. A few miles of road work—actually in a big pasture—showed the bronc what was expected of him. The rider talked to him and gingerly patted his neck and rump. Sometimes on the first trip out, and sometimes not until the third, the trainer—the man on the big horse—handed the lead rope to the rider. Now the green pony and the rider were on their own. Whether the pony bucked a little or not, the worst was over and the pony was well on the way toward being a mannerly cow pony.

Every saddle horse has to go through similar preliminary training. The brightest, quickest, and best-shaped are given extra training to develop the special skills required of roping horses, cutting horses, and rodeo horses such as those ridden by pickup men, bulldoggers, and trick riders.

Driving once across the smooth buffalo-grass plains of the Panhandle of Texas before it was plowed under to make way for wheat, I met a lone horseman. I stopped my car and we talked a while. I learned that the handsome horse he rode was a Quarter Horse of the Peter McCue strain. The lanky, soft-spoken cowman mentioned the animal as if the horse were a young man in school.

"Oh, yes, this fellow is a pretty good cow pony," he said in answer to my question, "but he is only five years old and has lots to learn. He's being schooled for a roper. Every chance I get, I give him more instruction."

As I drove away I thought about his attitude toward his pony and how important a well-trained horse is to the man who works with him. The horse has to be as expert as the rider. As with his war-horse ancestors, the cow horse must take part in sudden violent action, working as a partner with the man on his back. This is very true of roping horses whose training sometimes takes several years.

After he has had the basic training of a cow pony, learning how fast cattle can run and how to dodge and head them off, the student roping pony is ready to learn the finer points of his trade. He must learn when to turn the speed on and off. When a quick dash is over he must relax and be calm, in order to save his wind and strength for another burst of speed.

As he goes about his work, the cowboy on him plays with the lariat. He swings the end of it past the pony's head, flipping it close to an eye. When the rope first hits an ear or an eye or the side of its face, the pony shies sideways or even tries a buck or two. But the day soon comes when he is so used to the rope that he never bats an eye as it goes whizzing past his head. The cowboy drags the lariat over the pony's hips and lets it dangle so that it touches his belly and legs. This too, the pony gets used to.

The cowboy swings the loop overhead and puts the pony into a fast run. He then sends the rope flying out at a shinoak or a small sagebrush. If the pony can't be stopped in time, and he jerks the bush from the ground, the sudden pull on the saddle and the bush sailing at him may give the horse a bad fright. But after it has happened a few more times, it no longer bothers the pony, since he didn't get hurt. In further training the roper races half way across the corral, casts the loop, leaps from the saddle, and grabs the rope. While pulling on the rope as a calf would, he motions with his hat or hand for the pony to pull back on the rope. A little rope about the horse's neck, through which the lariat is passed after being tied to the saddle horn, pulls the horse's head around, forcing him to face the calf—or the cowboy who is playing the part of a calf.

As training of the cow pony goes on, anything that gets in the way is likely to have a loop thrown at it by the trainer. Dogs, goats, pigs, turkeys, and of course calves, suddenly find the student roping pony carrying a cowboy swinging a rope bearing down on them.

When he has finally "graduated" to roping calves in an open pasture or in a rodeo contest, the pony can take off like a shot and bring his rider close for the throw. After the catch is made, the cowboy leaps off the instant the pony comes to a sliding halt. The rope which has been tied to the saddle horn jerks the calf to a sudden stop, but does not jerk him off his feet. The cowboy "runs down the rope" and throws the calf by hand, while the pony keeps a steady pull on the rope. If the pony pulls too hard, the calf will be dragged. If the pony doesn't pull hard enough, the calf can get to its feet while the cowboy is trying to tie its legs.

One forefoot of the calf is tied to both hind feet with a little rope called a "piggin' string," and then the calf is "hogtied." We suppose hogs were once tied that way—anyway, cowboys use the expressions "piggin' string" and "hogtie" even though they are talking about calves.

In a contest where speed is most important the cowboy holds this "piggin' string" in his teeth so it can be easily grabbed when needed. A man roping on a ranch where there is not such a hurry would carry it wrapped around his waist. Calves usually weigh from two hundred fifty to three hundred pounds, so it is easy to see why a cowboy needs the help of a good horse in order to hold one.

Some well-trained roping horses can throw steers that weigh more than they do themselves. The cowboy cannot, of course, dismount and throw a steer with his hands (unless he is a bulldogger and that is an entirely different stunt and never done on ranches). After being roped, a steer has to be thrown by the horse, which races off at an angle so that the steer hits the end of the rope and goes heels-over-head. It is rough play. After the steer goes down the pony has to pull back very hard to keep the steer from getting to his feet while the cowboy runs in to hogtie him as he would a calf. To-day, steers are very seldom roped and thrown on working ranches, or even in rodeo shows. Steers can be injured in the falls, men can be jerked clear of the saddle, and horses can be whipped off their feet. Cinches can break.

In Wyoming, at the Cheyenne Frontier Days Rodeo, I once saw a saddle ripped from a pony's back when a big steer hit the end of the line. The cowboy sailed through the air and was dragged almost fifty yards before he got out of the saddle. He suffered only a few scratches. Any man who attempts steer roping must be as tough as rawhide.

The most unusual roping story I know was in a letter from a dear friend—Mr. Joe Williams of Amarillo, Texas—who died in 1957. When he was a young man, Mr. Joe was ramrod, or manager, of the Ro Range, as the ranch lands of Alfred Rowe, an Englishman, were called. Mr. Rowe told my friend this story, and this is the way Mr. Joe passed it on to me.

In 1886, Jesse Broadnax, a boy perhaps twenty years old, came un-expectedly upon a lone surviving . . . huge buffalo bull. He was crossing a dry creek [an arroyo] afterwards named Jessarroyo in honor of the fearless cowboy. Jesse was mounted on a small pony about fourteen and one-half hands high, weighing perhaps eight hundred pounds. The buffalo bull weighed about twice that much. Jesse was without a gun but he was not to be daunted . . . so he proceeded to rope, throw and hogtie the bull and slay him with his pocket knife. There was no grandstand of admirers to cheer and encourage him in his dangerous task.

With the hide and horns as trophies, we can be sure Jesse became the tall man in the bunk house.

The pony was later in my mount [the string of four to ten horses each cowboy rode in turn was called his "mount"], and we called him "Little Jess" after his trainer who had moved on to Montana. He was a little flea-bitten bay Spanish pony without a mark of Thoroughbred ancestry about him, but his intelligence was uncanny . . . I rode him when riding was difficult and hazardous.

Here is a probable explanation of how Little Jess, with his eight hundred pounds, could throw a sixteen-hundred pound bull: After the noose settled over the buffalo's horns, Jesse flipped the lariat to the offside of the buffalo's back. Then he spurred to the left. This pulled the rope taut as a fiddle string across the buffalo's hocks, or heels, and jerked his head to the right, spinning him head down as he went off his feet. Cowboys call this rough kind of throwing "busting a steer." Thrown this way the animal flops over so hard he has the breath knocked out of him for a moment, giving the cowboy a chance to hogtie him.

Roping horses were, and still are, beloved members of every ranch family. Cow people are not ashamed of the fondness and sentiment they show for their horses. Once, when driving south of Cheyenne, Wyoming, I noticed a small plot fenced off with barbed wire out in a vast open prairie. I was curious and went over to investigate. A wooden marker, weathered and split, stood at the head of a grave. The date was worn away but the words, still readable, were:

HERE LIES OLD BLUE—MAY HE REST IN PEACE—THE FINEST PONY
THAT EVER STRETCHED A ROPE.

The cutting horse is another specialist in the cow business. His training starts out the same as the other cowponies. Then, when he is about four years old, if his owner thinks he has talent, a quick mind, agility, and the willingness to work for perfection, he is started on specialized training. The object is to make of him that super holder and header of cattle, a cutting horse. His job will be to cut cows, calves, steers, and bulls out of herds and to see that they don't turn back. When he is fully trained, he will be the most prized horse on the ranch, and now that rodeo shows have cutting horse contests which make it possible to win big money for a few minutes work in the arena, the cutting horse is the prince of ranchdom.

The next time you see a cutting horse perform in a rodeo, or a film of a rodeo, notice how he works without being guided by his rider. Watching his amazing speed and concentration, and seeing him outguess the steer at every turn, is a delight for all horse lovers.

One summer some of the young, unseasoned cowhands and I were trying to cut out some longhorn steers from a big herd of more civilized white-face cattle. It was a hot afternoon and we had gotten the cattle excited,

which added to our difficulties. Mr. Carter, who owned the ranch, rode over
and as soon as he saw what was going on, ordered us out of the herd.

Mr. Carter didn't like having good meat run off his beef cattle. He had
contracted to pasture the longhorns through the summer, but he had not
counted on the tough brutes breaking down a pasture fence and getting all
mixed up with his white-faced Herefords. Now, to cut them out was a
troublesome task, and it was no job for novices. While the cattle quieted
down we all waited in the scant shade of a windmill for one of the boys
to bring Mr. Carter's own cutting horse, Major.

When the horse was led up and saddled, Mr. Carter mounted and he
and "Mage," as he called him, moved into the herd with quiet assurance.
We soon saw that we, as well as our horses, were far outclassed. The old
white-haired, weather-beaten rancher rode with swinging reins; any direction was given by a slight shift of weight in the saddle. After he pointed

"Mage" at the steer he wanted, he let the horse do the rest. Mr. Carter just sat straight and easy and almost seemed to be along just for the ride. He did help the horse by staying in balance and keeping in rhythm with the sideway leaps, forward plunges and pivoting movements to block the steer. "Mage" would thrust out a foreleg like a boxer throwing a punch, then catch his weight on it and turn. He weaved through cattle like a broken-field runner avoiding a tackle in a football game.

When he got the steer out to the edge of the herd, "Mage" reached out and clamped his teeth on the root of the steer's tail. With a nip he gave the twisting squirming animal the bum's rush into the clear and toward the cutout herd. Then he turned and proudly, but calmly walked back. He was blowing a bit. What he had done is perhaps the most concentrated fast action a cow horse is ever called on to do. Unlike a race horse, the cutting horse can quiet down immediately after hot and furious action.

When Mr. Carter rode into the herd for the second time he didn't need to direct "Mage" to a longhorn. The horse now knew that longhorns were the ones to be cut out, so he moved in behind the first one he came to that was in a good location to be scooted out of the herd, and quickly headed the steer off every time the beast tried to turn back.

The admiration cowmen have always had for cutting horses seems to stop just short of idolatry. When they tell about their favorites with the usual Western flair for extravagant overstatement they fully expect their listeners to discount some of their remarks. I have heard various forms of the following comments made with very straight faces:

"Why, Brown Charlie is so smart he could run this ranch single-handed —if he only knew how to get a bank loan." Or, "My cutter can read brands better than any cowpoke on the place." Or, "He'd do the job of separating those steers just as well without me; I just go along for the ride." And so on.

CHAPTER TEN

The Mustang Does His B

The task of building a large part of our nation out of an empty land lay ahead of the people who pioneered the West. It is amazing that so much was done in a bare hundred years. A new type of American, the Westerner, came into being as the West was settled: exuberant and confident, keyed to action. There was much to be done. There were many miles to cover.

County and state and territorial governments were set up, land surveyed, officers elected. Towns, homes, ranches, and farms bloomed on the prairies. Sod was broken, wells dug, land fenced, and windmills rose to become landmarks in the lonely, high and dry stretches.

Throughout all this hard work the mustangs were caught and trained to be of help. The country had to be civilized as well as settled. The wide open frontier country with its boom towns and easy going ways had become the hideout and the prey of a small but violent criminal element. Some of the troublemakers were men and women from the underworlds of cities farther east who had come to the boom towns to get easy money, no matter how. At a time when many men carried firearms, any quarrel between Southerners and Yankees might lead to bloodshed. The recently ended Civil War had stirred up hatreds that still smoldered.

Others who frequently had run-ins with the law were happy-go-lucky unschooled range boys who had taken too readily to saloon life and to the handling of six-guns.

Controlling these lawbreakers meant that a few determined, fearless men in every county had to pin stars on their vests, saddle up their ponies and go in pursuit of the bad men.

Some motion pictures, television programs, and novels have so exaggerated the old days of the West that it is difficult for us to think of those heroic actions as having actually happened. Yet they did, and the mustangs were right there playing a big part in the drama. They carried both the "good guys" and the "bad guys." Often the horses were pushed to the very limits of their endurance, and sometimes they were shot down along with their riders when the bullets started to fly.

Every peace officer of the Old West could tell about some special, loyal, untiring pony friend that stayed under him when the going got tough.

One such peace officer was William "Bucky" O'Neill whose saddle horse, Sandy, was as gallant as his master. Bucky was a good looking, well-educated, well-read, kindly man who rode through his part of the West in the 1880's and 1890's like a knight-errant.

Once, when he was sheriff of Yavapai County, Arizona, a train was robbed in Canyon Diablo, and Bucky jumped on Sandy and went in hot pursuit of the bandits. Even with the help of Tom Horn, the famous army scout, and a posse of deputies, the chase went on for days. Several times the posse closed in, and bullets flew both ways. One of the outlaws was killed. Others escaped and the man hunt continued. Twice Sandy swam the Colorado River with Bucky on his back. Some of the deputies' horses wore down and had to be replaced, but Sandy not only kept going, he continued to lead the pack. Sheriff Bucky O'Neill was far ahead of his own men when he trailed the bandits into Wah Weep Canyon. Alone that night he dismounted and hid Sandy in a canyon nook. Then with the stealth of a mountain lion Bucky circled the hideout of the tired outlaws. They were resting and completely off guard when Bucky leaped out and got the drop on them.

As one of the bandits explained it later, "We were so sure we had made a clean getaway, we were half asleep when Bucky jumped out from nowhere and said, calm as you please, 'Lo, boys, what's new? Stick 'em up.' "

Sheriff Bucky O'Neill held the outlaws under his gun for an hour before his deputies arrived, and was still astride the enduring Sandy when he rode into Prescott with his prisoners. Bucky helped organize the famed Rough Riders who served under Theodore Roosevelt in the Spanish-American War. He was killed in Cuba, during this war, at the age of thirty-eight.

The race after bandits was not always on horseback. When Lieutenant Reynolds of the Texas Rangers went on the trail of the notorious Sam Bass Gang, he rode in a buckboard pulled by a span of wiry mules. Reynolds was recovering from a bout with fever and was too ill to ride. Eight of his men rode alongside on horseback.

The nine men started out about dusk on a July evening. Seventeen hours and one hundred and ten miles later they pulled into the hot, dusty town of Round Rock, Texas. When they arrived they found that the whole grueling trip—a merciless test of their horses and mules—had been for nothing. Just before Reynolds and his men came into town, Sam Bass and one of his gangsters had killed two local deputies. Texas Ranger Dick Ware was sitting in a barber shop waiting for a shave when he heard the shots. He rushed to the street and with deadly accuracy ended Sam Bass's murderous career just as the outlaw was mounting his horse to escape.

As the years went by the long rides, the big cattle drives, the big open range, the big bad men, and the big mustang herds were all cut down to size and the West settled down to become a work-a-day place. The horses ridden by cowboys and wranglers and other horsemen were generally ranch or farm bred, and more often than not, had mustang heritage, although the improving of stock was going on all the time by bringing in good Quarter Horse and Morgan and Thoroughbred sires.

As the West grew there was endless work to be done and the Arab-Barb-Andalusian-Spanish-mustang-Western-Quarter horses did their share of it. Winter and summer one saw them on the lonely roads hitched to every kind of vehicle, including the curious little canvas covered hacks used by the United States mail carriers.

If you knew our local doctor, you knew his sorrel buggy team. And if you saw them coming toward you on one of the grooved roads worn in the prairie, you pulled aside to let the buggy pass. More often than not, Doc would be sound asleep with the reins wrapped around his folded hands, depending on his beloved sorrels to get him safely home.

People from the East who were used to larger carriage horses were always amazed at what the mustang teams could do. My father used to remark that some of the ponies were so small you had to tie knots in their tails to keep them from going through their collars. However, their size was unimportant when one saw how well they covered ground. Anyone who rode behind a team of mustangs in a top buggy over rough roads for forty or fifty miles in a day was greatly impressed by the endurance and willingness of these Western ponies.

When cars and trucks and tractors came into use, one heard people say the horse would soon be a thing of the past. But it didn't work out that way. Machines merely relieved horses—as they did people—of a lot of stupifying drudgery, so fewer draft horses are needed, but there are more saddle horses today than there were fifty years ago.

It was only natural that the *vaqueros* and cowboys who met at roundups and fiestas and fairs would test their skills against each other and show their trained horses. Such contests first became popular in California among the Spanish ranchers and their *vaqueros*. Our word, "buckaroo," is simply a mispronunciation of *vaquero,* the "V" having a sound almost like a "B." The California roundups were called rodeos, and competitions all over the country began to use the name. Rodeos were an incentive for cowboys to perfect their skills and take great pains in training their horses. By 1880, there were ropers and riders of bucking horses who had gained great local reputations. In the 1880's both Denver, Colorado, and Cheyenne, Wyoming, held rodeos for which an admission charge was made. Then in 1888, a full-fledged rodeo was held in Prescott, Arizona, in which the events were competitive with cash prizes going to the winners. No doubt the public-spirited Bucky O'Neill was one of its enthusiastic promoters.

Soon girls were getting into rodeos as contestants. In 1901, "Prairie Rose" Henderson, a rancher's daughter, entered the bronc riding contest at Cheyenne, Wyoming. She did so well and got so much publicity that the cowgirl bronc riding event became a feature at many rodeos.

Today several western universities give more attention to their rodeos than they do to football. Hundreds of young men and women go in for trick riding, roping, cutting horse contests, barrel races, and other rodeo events. It is not at all unusual to see an English major or science major, or perhaps a pre-medical or law student ride a bucking bronco or rope and tie calves with all the form and sureness of the professional. Girls generally avoid the bronc riding and calf roping events, but are enthusiastic competitors in cutting horse, barrel racing, and trick riding events.

Many rodeo events call for as much co-ordination and skill and daring as did the jousting matches of the knights of old. And they are certainly more democratic. Ranch owners, ranch hands, Indians, and tender feet from dude ranches—anyone who can qualify and put up the entry fee can enter. The only exclusive and aristocratic beings that take part are the highly trained and often highly bred horses. Few people's ancestry can be traced as far back as that of some horses! The Quarter Horse breed predominates in the rodeo world. Parade horses, roping horses, cutting horses, bull-dogging horses and the mounts of the pickup men and the trick riders are nearly all registered Quarter Horses or of Quarter Horse breeding. All are as carefully trained and cared for as polo ponies or racehorses.

The bucking horses are, however, an exception. They are far from being aristocratic. Most of them come from the northwestern United States and Alberta, Canada. They are hardy, delinquent mongrels—sort of "dead-end kids" of the horse country. They get their fighting spirit and quickness from their Spanish war-horse, mustang forebears. They get their weight and height and heavy bones—they average fifteen hands high and about twelve hundred pounds—from the cold-blood draft breeds which came to the Northwest with the settlers.

Dappled gray Percherons, the French draft breed, and the heavy Belgians were interbred with the Spanish-blooded Indian ponies. Some escaped and joined the roaming mustangs. The mixed-blood horses that resulted were heavily muscled, and short-coupled. Some are called "chunks" and others, because their feet are so much bigger than those of the light saddle breeds, are called "puddin' foots." In districts where the huge Clydesdales of Scotland mated with the mustangs, their offspring are blocky and ungainly. Their type is known as the "Oregon Lummox."

From these strong, stubborn, and often fierce horses, with their wildly mixed heritage, came many of the famed rodeo buckers. Good bucking horses are not made; they are discovered. Unbroken wild horses do not necessarily make the best buckers. Most horses will tame down after being bucked out week after week. But a true bucker never gives up the fight to keep men from riding him. Some are natural outlaws, never to be tamed. Others that explode out of the chutes with demonic violence and never let up until their rider is rolling in the dust are gentle and easy to handle away from the arena. It is not uncommon to hear of buckers that were once gentle enough for children to ride, before something changed them.

The great Midnight, who lives on in the memory of many bronc riders who have long since hung up their spurs, once belonged to a country schoolteacher in Canada. One day a tumbleweed blew across his path. The horse was so startled he began to pitch and his schoolteacher owner was thrown. After that Midnight bucked at every opportunity. He was no longer of any use so he was sold, but the honest teacher explained why he was selling the horse. The buyer, equally truthful, explained why he was buying him, saying that he had heard about the horse's habit of bucking and that he wanted him for a rodeo bucking horse. So Midnight got into show business and made good. He tossed the best busters in the world. Only a few stayed with him the required ten seconds, and this must have happened on his off days. When he died, his grave was marked with a marble monument on which the epitaph ended with the words, "If there is a hoss heaven, Please God, rest his soul." Two namesakes, Five Minutes to Midnight, and later on, Ten Minutes to Midnight, carried on in the tradition of the master.

The buckers are supposed to be the villians of the rodeo show, but sometimes the crowd forgets and roots for the horse instead of the rider. In 1937, the New York *Times* carried a news item headlined, "Five Minutes To Midnight unridden at Cheyenne Frontier Days Rodeo. He is still King of Buck. The twisting, sunfishing bronc dumped Burl Mulkey right in front of the grandstand to the cheers of 15,000 spectators."

Badger Mountain was another famed bucker—a natural outlaw. In 1944, he threw his two hundred and ninety-fifth man. During his ten rambunctious years in the business, only five bronc twisters stayed with him for the ten-second count.

Although they are the villians of the show, the bucking stock are given the best of care. No race horse lives such a life of ease. The buckers work only ten seconds at a time and only once or twice a week during the season—then they get a long winter vacation. Some of them are so snooty—or so mean—they are given a paddock to themselves or one that is shared with only one or two other horses they happen to like.

During the years since Badger Mountain tossed so many men in the dust, hundreds of bucking horses have had their rousing show-bill names blared out of the loud speakers at the arena side. Hell's Angel, Steamboat, Cold Deck, Widow Maker, Chief Tyhee, Trail's End, Jake, and Jesse James—to mention only a few of the great ones which erupted from the chutes. On the backs of every one of them daring bronc riders have spurred through a tornado of action trying to stay aboard for the seemingly endless ten seconds.

The contest between man and horse is always a breath-taking spectacle, and the result can never be foreseen with certainty, for, "The hoss ain't livin' that can't be rode—and the man ain't livin' that can't be throwed."

CHAPTER ELEVEN

North of the Cimarron

The year I was fourteen looms large in my memory of the mustangs. It was the year a herd of my father's was taken to the country north of the Cimarron River.

Dad had been in touch with Mr. Harvey, a rancher friend in western Kansas. The market for horses there was pretty good, Mr. Harvey wrote. Farmers and small ranchers were in need of good mustangs. They could break them out for cow ponies and for general use around the farm. Mustangs were good for buggy and light wagon teams, and for children, to ride to school and on errands.

The horse market was slow in Oklahoma that year, so my father decided to send one hundred and fifty head to Kansas to be auctioned off.

We always seemed to have a few too many mustangs in our pastures. Bob Porter, his helper, and occasionally Mel Cummings—a ranch hand— broke and gentled them and many were sold. But my father couldn't resist buying more when he saw a new bunch from the wild herds of New Mexico being unloaded in the stockyards in our town of Woodward.

If a pasture was not being used he hated to see the grass going to waste.   *107*

Besides Dad liked being around horses. He didn't have a hobby as other men did; the mustangs were his hobby. As for me, at that age, I could think of practically nothing else but horses.

For days the conversation in our house centered around the mustangs and the overland journey they were to make. There were many things to discuss. Who would be the wranglers? Who would drive the chuck wagon? What saddle horses would be used? And most important of all in my mind was the question, Would I be allowed to go along as one of the wranglers?

At every opportunity I mentioned all the reasons I could think of to show that I was very necessary to the success of the trip.

"I know," Dad agreed, "you're a pretty good camp cook. You ride well. You're getting sort of handy with a rope, and you might be helpful generally. But this is going to be just a lot of hard riding—a rough, hurried trip." He paused, then added another reason with which to dash my hopes. "And, after all, there is the Cimarron to cross."

Mother and grandmother, my sister Russell and younger brother Benton, looked up with concern. People in our part of Oklahoma didn't take the Cimarron lightly. It could be treacherous. In some places there was quicksand to trap the unwary. Holes and whirlpools were found in unexpected places. Sometimes it was deep enough to swim a horse and at other times you could ride across the river without getting your boots wet.

The Cimarron is an odd and mysterious river. In the Black Mesa country, in the most western part of Oklahoma, it winds past canyons with petroglyphs carved on the walls that link the people who made them with the early Mayas of Yucatan. There are dinosaur tracks in a creek bed not far from where Kit Carson once set up a military post.

Further down it skirts the Glass Mountains. These are gypsum-formed chimney buttes with selenite crystals that glisten in the glare of the sun.

In one place it meanders, or rages, depending on its mood, through shifting sand hills. The hills are pure, almost white sand, as free of vegetation as the Sahara. In fact, this district is now a recreation area, called Little Sahara, where one can ride a camel led by a good Oklahoman dressed up as a Bedouin.

One might think of it as a fairy-tale river if it weren't for the true stories of death and violence that occurred along its lonely stretches in the days of the pioneers.

I didn't want to get a discussion started about the hazards of the Cimarron! "Well, after all, I'm not a child," I said loudly. "If the others can ride across that old river, so can I."

"Remember," Mother cut in (she was not even going to mention the dread Cimarron, "that school starts the second week in September. If your delightful excursion with those silly mustangs lasts longer than planned, you will not be back to start school. And another thing," (she was thinking up more excuses) "you would no doubt drink water out of any old buffalo wallow. And—and you would be miles from help if anything happened."

I guessed she was thinking of Stirrup, a new light bay gelding I was riding, which had thrown me a couple of times.

"No, I think it is out of the question," Mother said with finality.

"But Mother," I wailed, "they need me. I know the tally book better than anyone except Dad and Bob Porter, and they won't be along. I promise to be back in time for school. And besides I—I want to go," I finished lamely and looked at Dad.

"Well, let's think about it some more," he said. "In the meantime there is plenty to do to get ready. Horses have to be fed more grain and put in top shape. Saddles and harness and things have to be repaired and checked over."

Two or three days later Dad came home from his law office with bad news. "Both Lou Jackson and Fred Munn have backed out of the trip," he told us.

Lou was a cowboy and occasional horse breaker, and Fred was a farmer who was going to drive the chuck wagon. Fred's wife had taken sick, and Lou had enlisted in the army.

"That leaves only Mel Cummings," Dad said. My heart sank. I pictured the whole thing being called off. But Dad brightened up.

"You know, I need a vacation," he announced. "And George is quite able to keep things going at the office without me for a while." George was a young lawyer who had been with the firm for about a year.

"I might go along and drive the chuck wagon," Dad went on. He was suddenly enthusiastic. "Anyway, I have thought all along that I should be there for the auction."

Mother and Grandmother exchanged smiles. They both knew how much he loved to be with the mustangs, and how he wanted to get away from the office and be out of doors.

With Dad going and men hard to hire, I saw my chances getting better all the time. I was about to plead my case when Dad continued.

"And if I decide to go, and, ah, be along to sort of look after him, maybe Paul could come with us." He looked at mother.

Her expression said as plain as words, "If you two have made up your minds, nothing I can say will change things."

Dad said to me, "Think you could wrangle alongside of Mel?"

"Oh, you horse-crazy harum-scarums," Mother said in exasperation. "I think Mel Cummings will have to look after both of you."

"Yip-pee!" I yelled and ran out of the house before anyone could change his mind.

The next day I gladly took the saddle and team horses, two at a time, down to Dave Reed's blacksmith shop to have new shoes nailed on. I liked everything to do with horses.

Standing at their heads, holding them quiet, and swishing the flies away, I watched big brawny Dave shape and fit the shoes. When he pressed the hot shoe against the foot to set it, the smell of burning hoof came up strong to my nostrils. I liked even that.

The chuck wagon was checked over and its brake shoes were replaced. Bows were set in the brackets to form a rounded tentlike cover when a new canvas sheet was stretched over them. Buckets and feedbags were put in along with sacks of oats.   cop. 10

When it came to supplying the kitchen cabinet on the back end of the wagon, Mother and Grandmother began to take an interest. They drove out with food and canned goods in a surrey to the pasture at the edge of town where we were outfitting.

The next morning the whole family got up early to wave good-bye.

Grandmother called out, "Take care now—have a good trip."

Mother cautioned, "Son, you watch that Stirrup beast, every blessed minute—you hear!" I was wishing Mel hadn't been there to hear that. Then she made it worse by calling out to him, "Melvin, now you'll watch after my boy, won't you? Don't let him take chances."

Mel looked a little embarrassed, and I slumped in the saddle, feeling about ten years old instead of fourteen.

On the way out to the pastures to get the mustangs rounded up, Mel didn't have much to say. I knew he wished he had Lou Jackson or some other grown man to help him. He did say, "For a bunch this size we ought to have three hands." I gathered he meant top hands like himself.

The mustangs were spread out along Sand Creek where they had lived

for several months. They were not happy about leaving. Mel said to work them out of the hills and breaks and down toward the creek. By dodging and turning and whooping and waving our hats, we finally got them moving together as a herd. To head off the ones that broke out and tried to run back meant one horse race after another. I was riding Gale, a chestnut Quarter

Horse type mare. Mel couldn't help but notice, I thought, that she was almost as quick on the turns and as fast as King, the dark bay gelding he rode. King was also of the Quarter Horse type, and the best horse we owned.

With mustangs, the first few hours of wrangling are the most difficult. They have to be shown they can't outrun or out-bluff the wranglers. They must be pushed hard—kept in a stiff canter until they find themselves bunched together trying to keep up with whichever one takes the lead.

In our case, a wild-eyed, snorting, square-hipped sorrel mare pointed up the herd. She took the lead and held it. She led all the way to Kansas— and as it turned out, all the way home again too.

After mustangs settle into a trail herd they are generally easy to manage; much easier, in fact, than gentle horses, because the gentle ones are likely to spread out and graze. When a horseman rides up to chase a mustang back to the herd, the mustang, being wild and fearful, will turn and run from him. A gentle horse, however, might just go on grazing or kick at a rider who comes up too close.

Dad had not taken the road by way of Sand Creek but had gone on ahead with the chuck wagon. It was past noon when we caught up with him some miles beyond the North Canadian River. He was sitting reading in the shade of a cottonwood tree. His leather briefcase filled with office papers was propped open at his side. Happy and Gray Goose, the wagon horses, were unhitched and busily munching grain in the morrals—the feed bags that hung on their heads. Stirrup and Baxter, our extra saddle horses, had been led along behind the wagon. They had finished their oats and were hobbled so they could graze.

Mel and I had been in either a lope or gallop most of the morning. King and Gale were dripping sweat and were flecked with lather. We unsaddled, and while I walked the two ponies back and forth to cool them out, Mel got a bucket of water. After we washed them down, each horse found a level sandy place and got down and rolled.

"The way they are rolling clear over from side to side, I guess we didn't hurt them any," I remarked.

Mel grunted. "That wasn't such a hard ride."

Mel certainly wasn't the breezy type—at least not with a kid like me.

Oats were poured out on a tarpaulin for Gale and King. When they were through eating they would be free to go along with the herd.

While we ate sandwiches and drank the lemonade mother had sent along, Mel and I described as many of the mustangs as we could remember so Dad could check them off in the tally book.

Dad wanted to get a good head start so that the herd wouldn't get in front of him, so right after lunch we helped hitch up the team and waved him on. An hour or so later we saddled up Stirrup and Baxter and started.

Stirrup was feeling his oats and "fighting his head" as the cowboys say. Twice he almost got his head down between his legs so he could do some real pitching. The thought of getting hurt if I was thrown didn't bother me nearly as much as the thought of Mel seeing it happen. I noticed Mel was keeping a sharp eye on me and my spooky pony. In order to quiet Stirrup down I did more than my share of chasing the wayward mustangs into line. Soon Stirrup's bright bay coat was dark with sweat.

Later in the afternoon the rolling sand hills through which we traveled leveled out onto firm red earth thinly covered with sage and bunch grass. The trail road skirted washouts and gullies and ravinelike breaks, then abruptly dropped down into a narrow canyon.

At a bend where the trail widened out into a valley we came to an open gate. Off to one side, Dad sat in the chuck wagon, again waiting for us. He was talking to Mr. Jeffries, the owner of the Red Canyon Ranch, who was sitting with his leg hooked over the saddle horn of a big cow pony. He had evidently arranged with Mr. Jeffries to pasture the mustangs overnight, because they waved us in and motioned toward the corral that was built into a curve in the canyon wall. After the mustangs had been corraled, we let them out the back gate into the pasture, a few at a time. This made it easier for Dad to check each horse against his description in the tally book. The brand, if any, and the color and approximate age, size, and anything else that would distinguish each one was listed. As I recall, we counted over sixty geldings, almost sixty mares, and twenty or twenty-five colts of varying ages.

It was dark when we finally finished supper. Stirrup and Baxter had finished eating their grain long before. They stood, heads down, and weary as though they were asleep on their feet.

I led them down to the pasture gate and with a slap on the rump sent Baxter in to join the herd. A bullbat swished by in the darkness. Off to the north came the faraway dismal howl of the coyotes. The cool night breeze of the high plains country sent a wisp of mane across my face. I reached up and pulled Stirrup's head over to my shoulder and patted him on the cheek. His warm muzzle brushed my ear.

"We're going to be good friends, aren't we, Stirrup?" We were in a strange place miles away from home. I sensed that Stirrup felt it too. He seemed to want to stand there and be close to me—he was in no hurry to catch up with Baxter. I tried to think how I would feel if I were in Stirrup's place. Would I like people? After all, people had roped and branded and gelded him and bucked him out. Did he think of humans as enemies?

"Are we always going to be friendly enemies?" I asked. "Well, whether we are or not, I like you, you rascal!" I added, holding his head hard against my own.

Back at the wagon, after spreading my blanket on a tarpaulin and rolling up in them, I thought of the things a pony has to suffer and adjust to and learn. Not long before, Stirrup had been a wild animal, running free. He was a Spanish mustang; a bright bay with black points—that is, his ears, mane, and tail were black, and his legs were black almost to the knees. The brand he wore was Spanish or Mexican. It was a picture of a stirrup, burned with a running iron—instead of a stamp brand—on his near hip. Of course that was the reason he was named Stirrup. The thought of the Mexican brand, big and sprawling, brought to mind a line from the "Strawberry Roan" song. ". . . and the map of Chihuahua all over his hip . . ."

Before he came to us, poor Stirrup had known bewildering fear and suffering in his struggle with men, I was thinking—and the boys out at the pasture corral must have handled him pretty roughly when he was being broken to the saddle—and . . .

I was deep in sleep when Dad shook me and called, "Up and at 'em!" A streak of light showed over the canyon rim to the east. The air was cool, and when I reached out I found my clothes and boots were damp with dew.

While I cooked ham and eggs, and made coffee, Dad and Mel rounded up the mustangs and drove them into the corral. Dad looked rested. He was having fun reliving the pioneer days of his youth. This was roughing it.

After we had eaten he said, "While we're traveling along, I might as well be giving some instruction to one of our mustang friends." He walked around looking through the corral rails. "How about tossing a rope on that fat and sassy blue roan gelding, over there. The one by the gate standing next to a pinto. I see a notation here in the book that he has been caught up several times and worked on a lead rope. He's estimated to weigh close to nine hundred and fifty pounds. Ought to make a good harness animal." Mel and I grinned. Here was action. "Let's go!" I called.

Dad did not say which one of us was to rope the roan so I rushed over and started to get the lariat off my saddle.

But Mel spoke up. "Better let me do it."

With the assurance of the expert he got his lariat and sauntered out to the center of the corral. There was a swirl of pintos, bays, browns, sorrels, duns, grays, and blacks as they raced in front of the red standstone cliff that formed part of the corral. Mel waited until the milling horses thinned out near the roan. Then the loop snaked out in the overhead "houlihan" throw and dropped neatly over the roan's head. I wondered if I would ever be able to make such a throw so well.

Mel's high heels dug into the ground to hold the roan as he was pulled this way and that. He yelled for me to ride on in. When I had Gale in close, the roan quieted down a bit and I was able to lean over and ease the lariat that was buried in his neck. Then I slipped a half hitch over his nose, took the rope from Mel, and dallied it about the horn of my saddle. Gale crowded the roan against the fence, and I was able to get another half hitch up over his head behind the ears. This improvised hackamore no longer choked him. It was easy to see that the roan had been led before because he came along without the hard fighting usual with a bronc going through the ordeal for the first time. Even so he was still spooky, and once or twice nearly jerked Gale off her feet.

When we were near the wagon, I held the roan with his chin snubbed close to the swell on my saddle while Mel and Dad put the heavy harness on him. At every touch and squeak of leather and every clink of metal the roan almost jumped out of his skin. When he was all buckled up I played out the rope so he could be bridled. Now he was ready for his first lesson. He was crowded against the wagon tongue and hitched on the offside of Happy. Happy was chosen for the breaking horse because he was larger

and more easygoing than Gray Goose. He would help hold the roan and keep him quiet.

Dad got in the chuck wagon seat and gathered the reins and let off the brake. Then with an "All right boys, let's go," the team moved out. The lead rope was still wrapped about my saddle horn. The roan champed at the bit in his mouth and danced and fretted. He lunged forward and sideways and tried to rear. Happy jogged along and seemed to pay no attention to his unruly teammate. Dad was talking to the roan beginner and was enjoying himself. After about half a mile the roan was less nervous. The winding road straightened out on open level country.

"Thanks, son," Dad called, "I think I can handle him all right from here on." I dropped back and handed the lead rope to him.

"Be real careful, Dad," I cautioned.

"Don't worry," he answered, grinning happily, "I'll be waiting for you ten or twelve miles up the road."

I turned Gale and rode back to help Mel get the mustangs pointed up behind the sorrel Judas mare. Lead mares were often called Judas mares because they led their trusting followers into the hands of the enemy—men—just as Judas had betrayed Jesus.

Occasionally Mel or I would have to ride up along the flank of the herd to point the leader to the right or left. It was a soft lazy day, with large cotton-wool clouds floating overhead. A drowsy stillness stretched for miles, broken only by the grass-muffled hoof beats and the whispering squeak of saddle leather. Far to the west, darker clouds were banking.

I got off and picked a prickly pear. As Gale jogged along I idly took the sharp spines out of it and bit a hole on the top edge so I could suck the tart juice. It tasted something like a green tomato. Up ahead a bronc jumped and snorted and darted sideways. No doubt a rattlesnake had given a startling whizzing warning.

We skirted a large prairie dog town. Mounds of earth dimpled the buffalo grass for over half a mile. Although the little animals amused us with their cunning scamperings and quick dives into their holes, we were glad to leave them behind. Prairie dog holes are greatly feared by riders. If a horse stepped in one while running, it could break his leg.

We were following a route that had once been the famous Dodge City Trail. Over this trail countless longhorn cattle had been driven to the shipping pens of Dodge City or farther north over the great Western Trail. Yet, aside from some grass-grown trail ruts, there was nothing to show the past of the prairie land.

I tried to picture the herds and the cowboys and the freighters and the cavalry troops that had passed this way so long before. Once it had been alive with buffalo and Indians and white hunters. Coronado and his armored knights had ridden across these very plains. And still, the prairies remained the same as they were in times past—an old and changeless land.

Riding along I had a good chance to observe the mustangs. Their moods and attitudes reminded me of people. Several sulky and bad-natured ones traveled along in a rigid gait with their ears set back. They were mad at everybody, threatening to kick or bite any horse that came too close. It was easy to see that they would be hard to train: stubborn and slow to learn.

Others simply looked bored and uncaring. Their sleepy half-closed eyes looked neither to the right nor left. This kind of mustang would, perhaps, be easy to break but would never amount to much as a helper.

Then there were the proud show-offs and the curious ones who kept well to the front or gallivanted about on the outside of the bunch, always looking ahead to see where they were going. With ears pricked forward they investigated every cross trail or meandering arroyo. They were the ones we had to race until we could head them off and wrangle them back to the herd. They were the ones who would fight hard when they were broken. But they were also the ones who would learn fast and become well-trained, useful, and gentle.

The youngest colts had all they could do to keep up with their mothers. But the yearlings and those a bit older were mischievous, always bubbling over with energy and high spirits. They nipped at each other and darted about, nickering and kicking up their heels. Some of the older horses acted annoyed at their horseplay.

It was a relief to catch up with Dad around noontime, and find that the bronc hadn't wrecked the outfit. There stood the roan already unharnessed and tied to a tree. He was tired and sweaty and looked dejected. His head was down and his ears were about half back. Most of the fight had gone out of him. He made no objection when I walked slowly up to him and patted him on the cheek. Dad said to turn him loose with the herd. A half day was plenty long enough for his first lesson in harness. When the hackamore was slipped off, he shook his head in relief and trotted over to join his friends where they had spread out along a narrow shallow creek looking for a place to drink.

Mel and I rode over to the drinking horses and singled out our afternoon mounts, Stirrup and Baxter. Very quietly, trying not to excite the others, we tossed our loops over their heads and led them back to the wagon. Gray Goose didn't have to be roped. As soon as he saw Happy eating, he hurried up and shoved his nose into his own feed bag.

That afternoon the clouds turned darker and the wind came up. Off to the west we could see that a thunderstorm was raging. We pushed on faster. The sorrel lead mare kept to the trail of the chuck wagon. We were crossing the big Selman Ranch. Since morning we had passed only two houses, far back from the road. Stirrup was acting like a gentleman. I wondered if he was trying to get me off guard so he could suddenly unload me. Once, when I seemed a little careless, Mel remarked that Stirrup was a tricky pony and would bear watching.

About six o'clock we came up to the chuck wagon. It was pulled up by a small log house in a clump of wildly waving cottonwood trees. The wind was blowing hard now. A corral and some open sheds were close by and a line of trees marked the course of a small stream. Dad was talking to a lanky cowboy. We were introduced and learned that Jim Hill lived alone in the line camp. Jim seemed glad to have visitors drop in. He said he hadn't seen a "livin' soul" for the last ten days or so.

"You'd better plan to stay here overnight," he said to Dad. "Might be a bit crowded, but the three of you can bed down in my cabin." We looked at the clouds getting blacker all the time. "It's sure enough going to be a gully washer." Jim commented.

Dad thanked him and said we'd be glad to accept his invitation. None of us had to be urged. We lost no time in getting our horses unsaddled and unharnessed and into the shelter of one of the sheds. The bed rolls were taken to the cabin and Dad roped the wagon sheet securely against the ever-rising wind.

All this meant more activity around his place than Jim was used to. He was busy also getting in wood and preparing for an evening meal.

"I think a little cream for our coffee would be a good idea," he announced as he dumped some coffee beans into an old fashioned grinder.

He looked at me and motioned to his own horse, a wide-chested black, standing still saddled by the corral fence. "If you'll jump on Squire there, and bring up a cow that has a calf by her, we'll just borrow some of the little feller's supper."

It gave me a good feeling to be asked to ride a real top hand's roping horse.

"Sure will, thanks for your pony," I said, as I climbed aboard.

With quick choppy steps Squire loped through the sagebrush until we came to a herd of cattle. I spotted a cow with a calf immediately. Every time she tried to turn back, Squire leaped to head her off and in this zigzag way we brought her up to the cabin.

Jim trotted over and said, "Thanks, I'll take over from here." As soon as he had taken my place in the saddle I heard the hard-twist rope whizzing as Jim played out a loop. Then with the greatest of ease he popped the noose over the cow's horns. Mel ran in and grabbed the lariat and moved down it until he had the cow by the horns. Jim leaped off Squire and picked up a small pail and while Mel hung on and wrestled with the lunging animal, Jim managed to milk a cup or so into the pail. The cow was a range animal and had never been milked before. Dad stood by the cabin door and laughed at the rodeo performance as the men grappled with the bellowing, fighting cow. Then Mel turned her loose and the cow gave out a plaintive "moo-o" as she and her calf went running back to the herd. Before I had Squire unsaddled and fed, the rain started coming down in big splashy drops.

While the rain lashed outside and the cottonwoods whipped back and forth in the gusty wind, the little one-room cabin seemed the coziest of havens. A few drips of water did start coming through the roof, but we soon had buckets and pans under them. Jim tied an old shirt around his middle for an apron and got a fire going in the small cook stove. While the oven heated he made biscuit dough. I set the table and opened some cans. Then I looked around at some of Jim's things.

It seems strange that a boy could find so much of interest in such a small room, but the movies with cowboys like Tom Mix and William S. Hart and Will Rogers and others were only beginning to make everyone familiar with cowboy gear.

With Jim's permission I tried on his bat-wing chaps—too long for me— and handled his lever action .30 caliber carbine. When Jim saw my interest in his holstered pistol that hung on the bed post, he thumbed the cylinder and ejected the shells before handing it to me. The heavy weight of such a hand gun always came as a surprise.

By the time I had examined his dress boots with their fancy stitching and the silver spurs that were never unstrapped from them, supper was ready. We pulled up the two chairs and a couple of boxes to the table. The food tasted good—even Jim's big soggy biscuits.

Mel and I did the dishes, while Jim caught up on the news with Dad. Men who lived far from towns always seemed eager to talk local news and politics with "the judge." Whether they were judges or not, most lawyers at that time were dignified by the title "judge."

After a while the talk just naturally got around to horses. Jim was curious about our herd. He knew a lot about mustangs, too.

"I've broke out several at various times, for cow ponies," he told us. "They usually have cow-savvy, and good common horse sense too, and are as quick as greased lightning, and can keep going longer than most men want to ride. Have one in my string right now. But he's an odd one. Somehow he missed out on the cow sense and the horse sense as well, but sure is quick and he has staying power. Something went wrong with his disposition or training. He just wouldn't settle down and learn any of the ranch trades like being a roper or a cutter. He has a mean streak in him. Has cold glittering eyes—I named him Snake-eyes. I never get on him but he tries to throw me."

I thought of Stirrup and wondered if he would always have a mean streak in him.

"But whenever I want to cover ground," Jim went on, "I always throw my saddle on Snake-eyes. The town I most often ride to is thirty miles away and Snake-eyes makes it every time in less than three hours. After he's made his try at dumping me overboard, he moves out in a long shuffling rack gait, and he never breaks it until we get there."

Every once in a while someone called attention to the storm outside. "Just listen to that rain come down," Dad said. "It sounds like a cloudburst. Buffalo Creek out there will be bank to bank by morning."

"How are we going to get the herd across—I mean after the rain lets up?" I asked.

"Swim them if we have to," Mel said. "You've swum horses before haven't you, wrangler?" he asked with a quick glance at me, and a one-sided smile.

I was pretty sure Mel knew I had never been on a swimming horse in my life, so I was glad when my father spoke up just then, making it unnecessary for me to answer.

"Oh, you boy's won't find it too difficult," Dad commented mildly. "Anyway, we'll have to push on, high water or not. The sale is set for the seventh."

Toward morning the rain stopped and the wind died down. We were out early and the sight we saw when the door was opened came as a shock. The little Buffalo Creek we had seen the evening before was now a river, perhaps one hundred and fifty yards wide. Roiling water with occasional clumps of brush and small trees swirled past.

"Are we going to cross that?" I blurted out.

Dad and Mel and Jim looked at me with amusement. They seemed not at all dismayed. To Dad I knew this crossing of the flooded stream would be another form of roughing it—of meeting a challenge of nature—of having fun.

Breakfast was ready when Mel and I came back, stamping the mud off our boots after having fed the stock. When we had finished eating I washed the dishes and put the cabin in order while Mel and Dad loaded the bed rolls in the wagon and hitched up the team. Then Jim saddled up Squire and rode with Mel and me to bring the mustangs in for the crossing.

As usual the sorrel mare—the Judas mare—took the lead. But when almost to the stream, she suddenly swung out on my side and made a break for the hills.

"Head her off! Head her off!" Mel yelled irritably to me. With spurs raking I had already put Gale racing after the lead mare. The footing was muddy and the sorrel was fast. For a moment it was uncertain whether she or Gale would win the horse race. Then I noticed that both Mel and Jim had cut across to help me head her back. When we had the herd bunched along the stream and quieted down, we rode back a ways and dismounted. Our horses were muddy and sweaty and already blowing hard.

"Thanks, Jim, for lending a hand," Mel said, and then added in a sort of grumbling tone, "sometimes one man and a boy aren't quite enough." He turned to me. "You've got to outguess these whiz-bangs. Start heading them before they get the jump on you."

I knew I could learn a lot from Mel, but I wished he would quit treating me like a kid. He made me pretty mad, and I must have shown it.

"Just swing together and you two wranglers will make out all right," Jim advised with an easy smile as his big bony hand clappped down on my shoulder.

That made me feel a lot better. I looked at Mel. He was checking the cinch of his saddle. Then he took his wallet and a pack of tobacco and cigarette papers and matches out of his pockets and wrapped them in a handkerchief. He put the bundle in his hat and pulled it tight on his head. He took the slicker from where it was tied behind the cantle of his saddle and removed a can of beans and a can of hash that had been rolled up in it. Next he took off his boots and socks and wadded a sock and a can in the leg of each boot. He wrapped the boots carefully in the slicker and tied it, tight and waterproof, back where it had been behind the cantle.

"Sort of fancy horse-swimmers, you fellers are," Jim commented. I had done everything that Mel had, except that I had no tobacco to stuff in my hat. But it had occurred to me that there were some lemon-drop candies in my jacket pocket that ought to be kept dry. So into my hat they went.

Jim was amused. "I always say to heck with it and ride on in, boots and all. Us Oklahomans are praying for water so much of the time, I just like to get saturated with it once in a while. Mostly when you ride up out of one of these streams you just have to dust yourself off."

"Well, in cloudy weather like this," Mel answered, as he buttoned up his brush jacket, "it would take boots a week to dry out. It'll be bad enough polishing saddle leather with wet jeans."

At Jim's suggestion Dad decided to drive downstream about four miles where there was a wide, more shallow crossing with a good gravel bottom. Jim said he would go along with him to see that he got across all right.

When our horses were breathing normally again we mounted. The stirrups were cold against my bare feet. With Jim's help we slowly hazed the sorrel lead mare into the water and, with a big whoop and lots of arm waving, the mustangs were crowded in after her. An opening in the trees downstream marked the other side of the crossing. Fortunately the lead mare headed for it. Before he got his boots wet, Jim turned back to join Dad. Mel called to me to loosen my saddle cinch. A swimming horse needs room for his lungs to expand.

A moment later I was to learn some more about how smart mustangs are. I knew that none of the colts in the herd had been in swimming water before, and I wondered if they would be in trouble, and how they would be able to buck the swift current. In the struggling mass I picked out the little heads of several colts and realized that every one of them was upstream of his mother. The force of the current, instead of washing the colts away downstream, washed them up against their mothers. I couldn't tell which one, the colt or the mother, had worked out this clever arrangement. When a mare hit deep water and began to swim, the foreleg of her colt in lashing out—and being pushed by the current—got up over her withers. In this way

the mare was able to give her youngster a piggyback ride. Then, when she found footing on the far side and started to climb the bank, the colt slipped his foot off her back and made it out of the water under his own power.

The place that was deep enough to swim the horses was only about forty feet wide. Before we got to it, Gale had been moving along in water shoulder deep and I was wondering just how good a swimmer she would prove to be. By watching the mustangs ahead I knew about when to expect the plunge. But even with warning it took my breath away when horse and saddle dropped from under me and cold water swirled above my belt. Gale's face and floating mane was all that I could see of her. At first she lunged forward and sank and lunged again—frog fashion. It was like riding a gently bucking horse. Then she evened out in a sort of dog paddle. It was great fun. But I realized Gale was burdened with a heavy saddle, so I slipped off and swam alongside with one hand hooked in her mane. As soon as her feet hit bottom and she started up the bank, I swung for the saddle.

The mustangs, all safely across, spread out and began to graze on the

open prairie. Mel was grinning when he rode up to me. Apparently he had enjoyed the swim.

"Well, wrangler," he asked as he jumped off and started to wring out his wet jacket, "how'd you like it?"

"I'd like to do it all over again," I answered. "And Mel, did you see how those colts let their mothers practically carry them across?"

I felt that Mel was finally beginning to treat me like a full-fledged wrangler. Mel took the things out of his hat and rolled a cigarette. As he let a puff of smoke drift out of his nostrils he looked at me closely and then suddenly began to laugh.

"If you could only see yourself!" He pointed at my face.

Baffled, I put my hand up to my forehead and it came away sticky. Then I jerked my hat off. Somehow the hat had been knocked out of place and water had splashed in. The lemon drops were a syrupy mess in my hair and a trickle of yellow syrup was running down my face. Mel roared with laughter. I laughed too but I felt like a kid again. And matters were not helped any when Dad caught up with us that evening and asked how everything was going.

"Oh, the Lemon-drop Kid and I are doing fine. We could wrangle a bunch twice this size," Mel replied as he slapped at the mosquitoes.

And as Dad laughed at Mel's explanation of my new nickname, I thought: A boy just can't win—one minute he's a top hand and the next he's just a kid.

That morning we had kept going in our wet clothes. But it had remained cloudy and we were soon chilled. Mel finally called a halt. We were out on the high plains with no trees or wood with which to make a fire. What sagebrush there was remained too wet to burn.

Mel said, "There is no way to get dry but there is a way to keep from catching a cold. Let's strip down, and rub ourselves and get up the circulation."

Soon we were standing stark naked by our horses, rubbing ourselves with our rough jackets which were almost dry. Our skins were fiery red when we dressed again in our damp clothes. Mel said it was an old frontiersman's trick he had learned from his father. "Never knew it to fail," he assured me. "We'll be warm now." And so we were.

By noon a hot sun had come out to dry us completely as we squatted by a small fire of sage twigs, eating hash and beans we had heated after opening the cans with our jackknives.

Late in the day I got my first glimpse of the Cimarron River. At this place it cut through pleasant rolling country and didn't look at all like the fierce stream I had expected to find. But when at last we rode along the bank, it did seem rather wide and I began to wonder what kind of footing was under the curling eddies and the little muddy waves.

When Dad drove up at dusk Mel and I were sitting by a smudge fire, and the mustangs were spread out along the bank of the Cimarron. The fire was not for heat, but to give us some protection from the mosquitoes.

After a quick supper we lay down and let the acrid smoke from the burning sage drift over us. We noticed that the horses were too bothered by the mosquitoes to graze. Most of them stood in pairs, head to tail, swishing their tails at the mosquitoes and stamping their feet. We got little sleep that night and our faces were speckled with mosquito bites when we saddled up early the next morning.

Dad had me ride along with him as he walked upstream to pick a good place to start the herd across. The river had run down almost to its normal level, but the Cimarron, I knew, was to be treated with caution and respect. I couldn't help thinking of a nineteen-year-old boy who had lost his life in this stream some months before. He had ridden in to see if it was safe for his mother and father and their family to follow in a covered wagon. The quicksand caught him and the current swept him under and he and his horse were never seen again.

"If there is any quicksand at this place, the herd will settle it before we take the wagon across," Dad pointed out.

Again Mel took off his boots and I was about to do the same when I noticed that a shoe on Gale's near hind foot was loose. Rather than get the tools out of the wagon and do a renailing job, I decided it would be quicker to pull the shoes off both of Gale's hind feet and catch up Stirrup and ride him. I was curious, too, to know how Stirrup would behave himself in the water. But I kept my boots on. I was not interested in finding out if I could ride him barefooted. As usual when I first mounted him, Stirrup tried hard to get his head down and do some bucking. He did get off a few cow-hops before I got him under control. Mel was watching him like a hawk and seemed even more concerned than Dad. But once we got the herd well started and we were moving through the water, Stirrup was as gentle as a kitten. He worked like an expert, too, dodging and turning and forcing the troublemakers into line.

To our surprise the dreaded Cimarron seemed tame. On we went through water that didn't reach my boot tops. Of course, I had quicksand on my mind.

In one place where the current seemed swifter, the mustangs dropped into deep water. Only their heads and floating tails could be seen. But it was only for a few feet and again they sloshed through belly deep water. Up front some of the mustangs began to struggle and flounder about. Now we're in for it! I thought with dismay. But luckily the ones who took the lead were always the strong and active ones. When it seemed a horse would surely go down, he went on fighting and lunging this way and that, keeping his feet churning the floating sand. Quicksand is fine sand that is kept in suspension by a current of water running under it. It tends to cling to anything that obstructs it while it starts settling toward the firm river bed. That is why each horse felt it was sucking him down when he tried to pull out his feet, which were held by it.

By the time the leaders had reached the bank they had so packed the sand it had settled to the clay bottom. The mustangs that followed walked through on a firm sandy bed. The colts—each one again upstream of its mother—followed at the back of the herd, so no quicksand trapped their small feet.

In order to keep the mustangs bunched, I rode farther out to the right. I forgot that I was leaving the settled sand path and getting out into quicksand. The next thing I knew, Stirrup had sunk down a foot or so into a pocket of quicksand and was lunging frantically. The more violent the action, the better, I thought. It will keep his feet from being caught firmly by the sand. So I raked far back with my spurs. Out in the open it would have brought on an explosion of pitching, and it did the same thing there in the water. But hampered by the clinging sand, Stirrup's exhibition of saddle bronc bucking, was in slow motion. With his feet hampered by the sand and with water to prevent him from putting his head down, of course he couldn't move very fast, but what he did was the best-known way to get out of quicksand. The flailing hoofs packed sand until it settled and the footing was firm.

When the entire herd was out of the river and spreading to graze, Mel and I quickly recrossed without any trouble. We each tied a lariat to the wagon pole, and when the wagon reached the deep place we were already across it in shallow water pulling on the ropes. Happy and Gray Goose, dependable as always, pulled the wagon to dry ground a few minutes later.

It was dusk when we drove the mustangs into a pasture. Dad arranged with the ranch owner to let our horses graze there until the sale on Monday. The chuck wagon was pulled off to the side of the old Dodge City Trail. We were tired and our horses were stumbling with exhaustion.

During the day a camp on the open prairie looks uncomfortable and helter-skelter: a saddle here, a skillet and a coffee pot there, bed rolls scattered about. But as dark settles down a strange change seems to take place. The bigness of the prairie is blotted out for the firelight illuminates only the things that are close by. The camp seems to become as small as a room.

That is the way it was with our camp that night. The wagon wheels and the propped up tongue draped with harness became a wall. The tarpaulins, spread over mounds of sagebrush gathered for mattresses, were transformed into divans with the saddles serving as pillows. Beyond the fire, the darkness hung like velvet draperies. Our home was safe and snug.

At breakfast the next day—it was a Sunday—we enjoyed watching what little traffic there was on the road. Once a Ford car chugged by. The people in it had on their Sunday clothes. A covered wagon was next to pass. Children peeked at us from under the wagon sheet. Extra horses were tied at the side of the team and a boy was herding along several more in the rear.

Dad waved to the driver and then remarked to Mel and me, "Horse trader," and added mock seriously, "a competitor." While Dad got shaved and into a dark business suit, I put his saddle on Gale, after nailing on her rear shoes. Dad was going to the Harvey Ranch eight miles farther on to see about the final arrangements for the auction that was to take place the next day. Mel had some friends in a nearby town and he set out to spend the day with them. I was to stay to watch our hobbled horses and the camp.

Before Dad left, he called me over to look at Gray Goose's foot. The fetlock joint was badly swollen, and he limped when I walked him around.

"We may have to buy a horse to take his place." Dad said. "Of course there's the young roan to use in a pinch, but I don't believe I'd trust him to pull me across the Cimarron on the return trip."

Dad was not happy about leaving me to spend a long boring Sunday alone, and, frankly, I wasn't looking forward to it either. I think he was trying to think of something that would entertain me. Anyway, he brought out his wallet and said, "Here's fifty dollars. You know, another horsetrader might come by this way. Maybe with a good well-broken wagon horse for sale. How about it? Do you want to pick out a horse and buy him?" He handed me the money. He really did have confidence in my judgment of horses. He had taught me himself.

"This is top price," he went on. "Of course, if you can get one for less, that will be all to the good." He hesitated, then added, "I leave it entirely to your judgment."

I could see that he was already picturing the dickering that would take place, and regretting that he wouldn't be there to share in it. To my father, buying a horse—even just an average work horse—was the greatest of treats.

After he rode off the hours dragged by, just as I had expected. No horse traders showed up. Some wagons and several surreys drove past. The people waved and I waved back. A Reo and later a Hupmobile—easy to spot by the high radiator snout—rolled along in the grooves of the high-center road. I fixed some lunch, then tried to sleep in the wagon, but the heat was stifling under the canvas cover. The ground under the wagon was a little cooler, but I still couldn't sleep, and the hot lazy day droned on. At last I went and saddled Stirrup. I kept muttering excuses to myself: this camp is safe; nobody in this part of the country would steal anything; we never lock up anything at home, not even when we are going for days at a time.

Thirty minutes later I was wrapping the reins of Stirrup's bridle around the hitch rail in front of a crossroads store. A half dozen buildings were clustered along a bare road that shimmered in the heat waves. It seemed to be a deserted place, but just in case someone was looking out a window I played the part of a seasoned wrangler. At the moment, I think I had in mind my hero, Charles Russell, the great artist and horse wrangler.

Across the broad sidewalk I walked with a ramrod gait, punching down my boot heels to make the metal weights on my spur shanks clink at every step. My yellow buckskin gloves were tucked into my belt. My jeans and blue shirt were faded and worn. My hat brim was rolled up and sweat stains showed above the leather band.

When I stepped inside out of the bright sun the gloom of the store blinded me for an instant. And when I could see, I didn't know what to say or do. For there at the rear of the store sat Mel with the store owner and his wife and a couple of young people about my age. Everybody was eating watermelon.

I had been feeling sorry for myself all day. Why was I the one to be left in a hot, dry camp? And now I had reason, I thought, to be angry. If Mel could come to town and take it easy and eat cold watermelon, so could I. I'd show him. I turned away before Mel could say anything to me. When I was seated at the counter I called out to the store keeper, "Will you please serve me some watermelon?"

"Why, sure thing, young feller," he replied. Everyone had stopped eating and I imagined they were talking about me, at least Mel was. The man put a big slice of melon in front of me.

"This is a sweet one, you'll like it," he said.

Mel called out, "Bring it over here."

"Thanks, but I've got to hurry back, I'll just eat here." Alone and aloof I ate my melon.

When I finished I called the man again and he sauntered up saying, "Yes, what can I do for you? How'd you like it—sweet like I said, wasn't it?"

"Yes, it was real good," I answered. "How much do I owe you?"

He looked puzzled, "Oh, you don't owe me anything. We're not even open for business on Sunday. You see, we've known Mel a long time and we all were just having a little get-together."

It now dawned on me that I had let my anger at Mel trap me into an embarrassing social error. Red-faced, I thanked the man and asked him to excuse me for barging in on a private family gathering.

When I was in the saddle I didn't let up on poor Stirrup until I was back at camp. To my relief the camp was just as I had left it; all was safe. The road was empty. In the shade under the wagon I tried to relax. The fifty dollars in my pocket seemed more than useless. Again I looked out at the road, and suddenly spotted a horse trader coming over the top of the ridge to the north. There was the covered wagon with extra horses tied to the team and strung out behind. A boy led three others, the last two of which were tied to the tail of the horse ahead.

A bay gelding the boy was leading looked pretty good to me. When the outfit came abreast, the driver pulled up out of the road ruts, stopped his team, spit out some tobacco juice and said, "Howdy." He was weather-beaten and scrawny with a large drooping mustache. A wide-brimmed black hat powdered with dust was pushed back on his head.

Thirty minutes later when he lifted the lines and whistled at his team through his tobacco-stained teeth, I was the proud owner of a fifty-dollar gelding. I could hardly wait until Dad returned so that I could show off my bargain, but I had to wait until dusk before he rode in. Immediately I led him out to where the bay was grazing on a long stake rope. Even in the fading light, one look was enough for Dad. He turned away and put his hand on my shoulder.

"Son, I won't beat around the bush," he said. "I'm sorry, but I think you were outmatched in that horse deal."

I was furious and unbelieving. "Why do you say a thing like that?" I demanded. "He's as strong as Happy—good legs—broad chest—sound as a dollar and—and you haven't even really looked at him."

"He's a balker," Dad announced. "And I'll tell you how I know. He has a terrier tail. He carries his tail turned up slightly at the tip. That means the tail has been injured."

"Well, what kind of an injury? And what difference does it make?" I asked.

"I think it is a special kind of injury." Dad explained, "And I found out about horses with that kind of tail, in the same way you're finding out, by once buying a balky horse. You see, some darned fools think they can start a balky horse by snipping off the tip of the tail with a jackknife."

He saw the shock and disappointment on my face, and he added quickly, "Now I may be wrong. I hope so. We'll try him out tomorrow."

I thought of one more argument. "But he has worked in harness. There are a few white hairs sprinkled on his shoulders. That shows he worked enough to get collar galls that later healed over."

"Yes, horses may work and be normal for a long time and then for some reason—usually mistreatment—they become balky. They get a determined stubborn streak, like some people. To cure them takes patient, gentle handling over a long period of retraining. Sometimes a great fright will shock them out of it, but seldom will an injury do any good.

I have seen ignorant men clip the last vertebrae in balking horse's tails, plug their nostrils with mud, reach in their mouths and make a little cut in their tongues so that they taste blood; all in the belief that the pain and fright will make the horses forget their balking. None of these tomfool cruelties are of any use. Nor will standing and beating a balking horse get him started."

The next morning Dad was proven right. The bay was balky. In the lingo of the ranch boys, "he wouldn't pull the hat off your head." So the bay—I named him Big Deal—traveled in the herd back to Oklahoma. There he was sold to a man who had just the right job for a horse of his determined temperament. Big Deal was put to work carrying the man's children to and from school. He was so big he could carry all three of them.

The result of Dad's trip to see Mr. Harvey was a worry as well as a big disappointment. He found that Mr. Harvey was very sick with typhoid fever, and had been unable to handle any of the arrangements for the sale as he had intended. Advertisements for the horse auction had not been placed with the local weekly newspaper, so when the sale came up three days later, it was a hit-or-miss thing. After selling over forty head at low prices, to a small group of bidders, Dad said we had better take the rest of the herd, still over one hundred head, back to Oklahoma. Dad had to get back to his office and I had to get back in time for school. Dad made a last visit to see Mr. Harvey, who was getting better, and early the next day we started back south with the mustangs.

The return trip was easier. The mustangs were trained to travel together in a well-bunched herd. The lameness went out of Gray Goose's foot but Dad used the roan in his place most of the time, except when we crossed the Cimarron River.

On the way back Mel and I became better friends. He still teased me at times and once in a while called me the Lemon-drop Kid, but I didn't mind it any more. I figured he was just trying to keep me from getting too big for my britches. But he did say he thought I had done my share and would some day be a top wrangler. That was a lot, coming from Mel.

The last day out, riding through Eagle Pass north of old Camp Supply, I got careless. I was relaxed in the saddle and the reins were swinging. Suddenly a badger scurried out of the sage practically under Stirrup's feet, and the show was on. Stirrup got his head bogged between his legs and pitched like a professional. In bronc-buster talk he "came unwound and swapped ends up in the sky as he sunfished and kicked at the stars."

I saw it all very clearly, because after the first few pitching plunges, I had a good solid seat on the ground from which to watch it! The remembrance of an old cowhand I had once seen thrown flashed through my mind. As he got up and dusted himself off he said in his slow but disgusted drawl, "You know, I believe that brute animal is of unsound mind. I think he's having a fit."

Mel had leaped off Baxter and was at my side. He looked frightened; really upset. Then I saw that blood was dripping from my chin. I guess Mel thought that the blood was coming from my mouth and that I was hurt inside. For a moment I was puzzled too, because I didn't feel hurt. Then I realized it was just a nose bleed. But Mel was pretty shaken up.

He kept saying, "It's my fault, Wrangler, it's all my fault. I should have told you more about that bronc."

"But what about him?" I asked as I looked at Stirrup where he was now standing, looking rather pleased with himself.

"Well, I guess you know most of it anyway. You know Jimmy Hinds, don't you? You know, Elaine's kid brother?"

"Why, sure," I answered, and was about to add I didn't know him very well, when Mel went on and said, "He's a mouthy little guy, so of course he told you how this Stirrup threw me once, and—well, I might as well tell you the rest. After he threw me I was so mad at that pony I rode him into the ground several times after that. On Sunday afternoons when a bunch of us fellows and girls would get together for a little rodeo. Well, I guess I made a bucker out of him."

Then, seeing that his news had not shocked me, he continued, "And thanks, Wrangler, for not making a big deal of it with your Dad. I know what a strict one he is about being gentle with stock."

"Stirrup isn't ruined," I said, wiping my nose which had stopped bleeding. "I like him for wrangling and for long rides. Maybe I'd never want to try and rope off of him, but he's my friend; my friendly enemy. I'll just have to watch him more carefully, that's all." I didn't get around to saying that I had not talked at all with Jimmy Hinds.

Mel gave a sigh of relief. He had gotten rid of a big load of guilt that had been bothering him, and making him uncomfortable around me. Still, I couldn't understand why he had been so upset because a horse threw him. Every rider gets tossed once in a while.

A few weeks after we got home, I was riding one Saturday near the Hinds's place looking for a filly which had got out of a pasture. It was not likely the young mare had strayed onto the Hinds's farm, which was well fenced, but I wanted an excuse to talk to Jimmy so I rode into the yard. Jimmy came running off the porch and down to the yard gate. He was younger than I and we didn't have much to talk about until he said suddenly, "I know that horse you're on—it's Stirrup isn't it?" He started to laugh. I waited, knowing Mel's secret was about to be revealed.

"One Sunday about a year ago, Mel Cummings rode that bronc over here." Jimmy said. "He and Elaine didn't know each other very well, but you could see he was real sweet on Elaine. They were kidding each other along and Elaine was acting real silly. Mel was sitting just like you are now, and Elaine was standing right here by the gate. They paid no attention to me. I was up on the porch.

"Well, I don't know what got into Elaine—girls do the darndest things—but suddenly she said, 'I dare you to gig that bronc with your spurs, Mel.'

"Well, no fellow is going to be buffaloed by a girl, so Mel came back with his spurs, and that sure pulled the trigger. As quick as a bullet that

horse took off, and Mel shot through the air and came clear over the fence and landed right by Elaine in the yard. She was sure frightened, but she helped Mel up. He wasn't hurt but he was mad and red as a turkey gobbler. I guess that got them acquainted fast, because they started going to movies and dances after that."

As I rode away I wondered how I would ever keep a grin off my face when I next saw Mel.

Late in the fall the mustangs that had traveled to Kansas and back were sold. I rode Stirrup out to round them up and drive them into a corral where the buyer and my father waited. Among the mustangs, when I found them grazing in a ravine, I noticed King, the wrangling pony Mel had ridden. Because of a saddle sore on his back, King had been turned out with the herd to give him a chance to rest up, and time for the sore to heal.

When King saw me and Stirrup, his head came up and his sparkling eyes and alertness told me he was happy to see us. As I circled the herd to bring the mustangs together it seemed very familiar and easy. Then I noticed a reason for it being so easy; I had another wrangler helping me. There, off to the side, was King, blocking and turning back the mustangs that tried to leave the herd, and hurrying up the slow pokes. Remembering the long trail drive, the mustangs fell in behind the sorrel Judas mare. All the time, King, very active and full of authority, was doing the job he was trained for—without a rider!

CHAPTER TWELVE

The Last of the Mustangs

As the West was settled, the mustangs, like the buffalo, were doomed to near extinction. The settlers brought about the changes that caused the mustangs to become smaller and scrubbier. The mustang breed first suffered when the mustangers captured the finest of the stallions. Inferior stallions took their place to father less worthy colts. Then the frontiersmen thinned out the predatory animals—wolves, bears, and mountain lions—which had formerly killed off the malformed and the weaklings among the mustangs. The freaks and weaklings lived on to have inferior colts. Then the settlers moved in and took over the best of the range land. The mustangs were forced to hide out in remote places where the grass and forage was of the poorest. Without much nourishment the mustangs lost height and appearance. There were, of course, exceptions. Some individual horses had all the beauty of build and grace of movement of their Spanish ancestors.

The Indian horses which had escaped from time to time to freshen the blood in the mustang bands had gradually been killed off during the Indian wars in the 1870's and 1880's. And finally the only mustangs left were the ones (like the herds from New Mexico which my father bought) that eked out a living in desert and mountain valleys far from the haunts of the white men. It is easy to see why the ones that were left deteriorated.

One little group of mustangs which had got cut off from the outside world were put on exhibition at the World's Fair in San Francisco in 1935. They were curiosities because they were not much bigger than dogs. They belonged to a man named Richard Tooker, whose distant cousin, Jack Tooker, wrote about how his cousin happened to have them.

The story goes back to about 1850 when a young Indian named Supais Smiley went to visit some of his Indian friends in a Supais village hidden in a canyon that branched off from the Colorado River. Smiley rode a pinto stallion and led a buckskin mare that was followed by her colt. There was no horse trail leading down to the village, so Smiley left his horses hidden in a nearby canyon and went the rest of the way on foot. When he returned for his horses, he found that an avalanche of rock had closed the only entrance to the canyon, and there was no possible way of getting his horses out. Thus the animals were doomed to live there in the canyon the rest of their lives. The mare eventually had other colts, and they in turn grew up and had colts of their own.

Every once in a while Smiley took other Supais Indians to the edge of the canyon to look down on the horses. The Indians were surprised to see how little the horses were getting. Smiley and his friends soon had the other Indians thinking that the ponies were sacred and must never be hunted or molested. They may have believed this themselves or they may have encouraged the idea in order to protect the little animals. In any event, the ponies went on year after year living in their sealed-off canyon; each generation smaller than the last.

When Smiley was an old man he met Richard Tooker, a prospector who was familiar with the maze of canyons along the Colorado River. They became good friends, and one day Smiley took Richard to see the ponies. But before showing him where they were, he asked Richard Tooker to promise he would never tell anyone about the ponies until after Smiley's death. Richard Tooker promised, and he was a man of his word. But he had no idea he would have such a long wait. Smiley lived to be well over a hundred years old.

It was not until 1932 that Tooker was free to tell others about the freak ponies and to try to get some of them out. The undertaking turned out to be very difficult because of the steep walls of the canyon, and because the ponies fought for their freedom like the wild animals they were. Finally, by using belly slings with block and tackle, Tooker and his helpers managed to get four of the animals out. One of the four ponies soon died from his frantic struggles. The other three were taken to the World's Fair to be exhibited. The ponies lived only about a year in captivity. After they died, their bodies were mounted for permanent display in a California museum.

Jack Tooker, in writing about these little mustangs, suggests why the horses became so small. In the canyon there were no mountain lions, wolves, or other wild animals to kill off the freaks and runts, as usually happened in a herd, so the less well formed lived to reproduce themselves, with all the bad features exaggerated by inbreeding. The shadows cast by the high, steep canyon walls kept the ponies from getting enough healthful rays of sunlight. Grass and other forage was sparse and lacked calcium and the vitamins needed for bone building. Several generations later—more than eighty years in fact—the stallions in the canyon were not much bigger than collie dogs; the mares were the size of sheep; and the colts were no bigger than jack rabbits. The better ponies were well proportioned and extremely active. They were miniature horses that leaped about the crags like mountain goats. But among the band were many freaks. Some had spindly legs and shrunken bodies. Some had big heads and legs so short their bellies almost dragged the ground.

In December of 1962, three miniature horses were shipped from Argentina to Washington, D.C., as Christmas presents for the children of Attorney General Robert F. Kennedy. Like the ponies of Smiley, these horses are of Spanish blood. They came from the ranch Haras el Peludo, near Buenos Aires, belonging to Julio Falabella. About a hundred years before, Julio's grandfather had turned out some stunted ponies to range by themselves. The more they multiplied, the smaller they got. Now there are four hundred of them, all about thirty-six inches high when they are fully grown. Exactly what vitamins the ponies lack, or what else caused them to become horse pygmies, is not known.

After ranches were well established throughout our West, the livestock raisers and farmers alike considered the mustangs to be destructive nuisances. Long before, the ranchers had captured the best of the mustang stallions and mares, using them for the foundation saddle stock of the entire west. With good horses, part mustang, part Morgan, part Quarter Horse, and part Thoroughbred, in their pastures the stockmen didn't want them to mix with the now lowly and scrubby mustangs. To prevent such misalliances the ranchers banded together and set out to exterminate the remaining mustangs. A bounty was offered for their ears just as it was for the ears of wolves and mountain lions.

But it took longer to get rid of the mustangs than the ranchers expected. Wherever and whenever the mustang *mañadas* were reduced to only a few in number, some enterprising mustang stallion would raid a farm or ranch and get some of the tame mares to join him. With blood from various breeds, the mustangs became an odd assortment of mongrel horses. Some had the big heads and clumsy, feathered feet and bulky bodies of the workhorse breeds. Some (the Hammerheads) had big heads and small bodies. Some were trim and patrician, showing the blood of the more cultured breeds. Others had the Roman noses of the cold-blood draft strains. Many were goose rumped with tails set too low, which indicated there was little left of their Arabian ancestry.

In 1924, a government agency estimated there were still over a million wild horses in the West, with the largest herds hiding out in the state of Oregon. The mustangers were encouraged to round up the free animals in great numbers when packing plants opened and offered a steady market for them. A big business developed in canned, smoked, and frozen horse meat. In the United States it was sold to feed dogs and cats, and much of it was shipped abroad for human consumption. In France, horse meat finds a ready acceptance, and it is not at all unusual there to see signs in the shape of a horse's head hanging over the butcher shop doors, indicating that horse meat is sold.

From the packing plants also came by-products like fine grained Cordovan leather from the horsehides, glue from the hoofs, and fertilizer and chemicals from the carcasses. A single Oregon packer slaughtered over a third of a million "fuzztails" as they called the mustangs.

The age of actual horse power was supplanted by the motor age. But it took an advanced type of motored device to finish off the mustangs. It took the airplane to hunt out and round up the last remaining wild bands. With men on horseback getting signals from men in the sky, even the most secret of hideouts was discovered. When the horsemen could no longer keep up, the airplanes buzzed the mustang herds and drove them to exhaustion or hazed them to the catch pens.

A few wild horses managed to escape even these persistent hunters. Under a Medford, Oregon, date line of February 20, 1936, appeared this item:

"A herd of one hundred outlaw horses led by six wild stallions created such a problem that stockmen asked the Jackson County Court today to approve a roundup. The stockmen say the horses trample down the range grass and alfalfa fields, eat the rock salt left for the cattle and kick the life out of sheep and young stock."

Far to the east of Medford in the valley of the Owyhee River in southeastern Oregon, the hunt for wild horses was still going on in the 1940's.

The only other place where mustangs roamed in large numbers was in Argentina, South America. The conditions were much the same there as they were in our West and the horses were of the same Spanish breed that were brought to North America. Fortunately, before the Argentina mustangs died out, a small group of Argentina horse breeders gathered together a herd of the best of the mustangs to be found. From them the Criollo breed of good looking, stylish, and active horses was developed, a horse type which in many ways resembles the Quarter Horse.

In Oklahoma, an effort is being made to preserve the last of the mustangs by establishing a registry for mustangs that carry an unbroken line of Spanish blood. It is too early to predict what success this effort will meet with. But the fine qualities of the Spanish horses live on in the most cultivated saddle breeds even though they are no longer of pure Spanish blood.

Although a few outlaw horses are still running free, or rather hiding out like bandits, the day of the real mustangs has long been past. The mustangs added an unusual chapter to horse history. They were a rare group of horses never to be forgotten by men who knew them.

About the Author

Paul Laune, a well-known illustrator, grew up in Woodward, Oklahoma, not far from what had been mustang country. When he was in his teens, his father bought herds of these rapidly disappearing horses, and young Paul was able to learn about them first-hand.

At that point in his life, Paul's interest in horses was equaled only by his interest in drawing, but as time went on, the artist in him gradually took precedence. He attended the American Academy of Art and the Art Institute in Chicago, and the Art Students League of New York, before studying in Rome.

Mr. Laune first worked as an advertising artist in Lincoln, Nebraska. In 1926, he joined the staff of the New York *Sun,* and was eventually made head of the Art Department. Since 1930, Paul Laune has devoted all his time to his work as an artist. His paintings and portraits have been exhibited in many shows, and he has illustrated countless books.

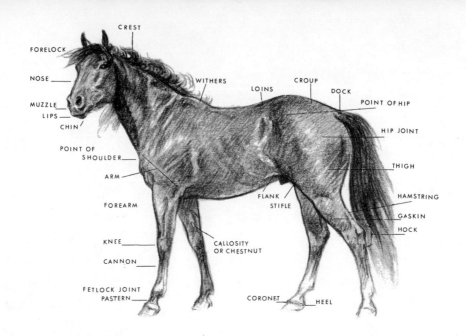

CREST
FORELOCK
NOSE
WITHERS
LOINS
CROUP
DOCK
POINT OF HIP
MUZZLE
LIPS
CHIN
HIP JOINT
POINT OF
SHOULDER
THIGH
ARM
HAMSTRING
FOREARM
FLANK
STIFLE
GASKIN
HOCK
KNEE
CALLOSITY
OR CHESTNUT
CANNON
FETLOCK JOINT
PASTERN
CORONET
HEEL

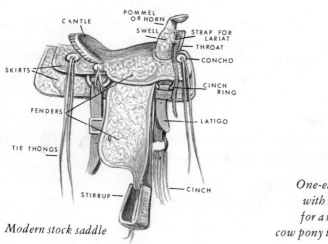

CANTLE
POMMEL
OR HORN
SWELL
STRAP FOR
LARIAT
THROAT
CONCHO
SKIRTS
CINCH
RING
FENDERS
LATIGO
TIE THONGS
STIRRUP
CINCH

Modern stock saddle

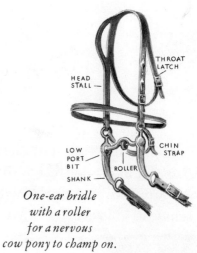

THROAT
LATCH
HEAD
STALL
LOW
PORT
BIT
CHIN
STRAP
ROLLER
SHANK

*One-ear bridle
with a roller
for a nervous
cow pony to champ on.*

SHANK
ROWEL

*Short shank,
blunt rowel spur*

*With the lariat, an
improvised hackamore
can be quickly fashioned.*

Index